'[*Irene Iddesleigh*] is a thing that happens once in a million years. There is no one above it and no one beside it, and it sits alone as the nightingale sings.'

BARRY PAIN

'I hope you will permit me to say how your perpetual freshness of phrase was to me a revelation of a new English style.'

R.H. TAWNEY

'I find the book [*Irene Iddesleigh*] enchanting. In my opinion it belongs away up – or away down, whichever may be proper – on the summit, in mid-sky or at the base of the foothills where sits serene the Sweet Singer of Michigan, Queen and Empress of the Hogwash Guild until now.'

MARK TWAIN

'She has quite a streak of something like genius.'

ASQUITH

'[*Irene Iddesleigh*] is written throughout in a vein of utmost magnificence before which Lyly, Bulwer, Disraeli and even Ouida pale their ineffectual fires.'

JAMES AGATE

'It is Irish prose, diseased. . . a perpetual warning to all writers with even a sixteenth part of Irish blood in their veins.'

ROBERTSON DAVIES

'My works are all expressly my own – pleasingly peculiar – not a borrowed stroke in one of them.'

AMANDA M. ROSS

'. . . gorgeously uninhibited prose.'

PETER QUENNELL

'. . . an Elizabethan born out of her time.'

ALDOUS HUXLEY

'. . . the personality who has disturbed the bowels of the millions.'

AMANDA M. ROS

'[*Irene Iddesleigh*] is. . . a better book than "The Outline of History", "May Fair", "Some Reactions of Colloidal Protozoids" and "The Chartered Accountants' Year Book for 1926".'

D.B. WYNDHAM LEWIS

'She cannot be altogether laughed off. She may be a long way from Shakespeare, but she partakes, in however infinitely minute a degree, of the Shakespearean power over language.'

ANTHONY POWELL

'. . . she was an artist, if a mistaken one. . . She had a rich and joyous sense of words, was indeed possessed by them.'

JAMES AGATE

'I expect I will be talked about at the end of 1000 years.'

AMANDA M. ROS

Thine in Storm and Calm

Thine in Storm and Calm

AN
AMANDA MCKITTRICK ROS
READER

Edited by
FRANK ORMSBY

THE
BLACKSTAFF
PRESS
BELFAST AND ST PAUL, MINNESOTA

First published in 1988 by
The Blackstaff Press Limited
3 Galway Park, Dundonald, Belfast BT16 0AN, Northern Ireland
and
Box 5026, 2115 Summit Avenue, St Paul, Minnesota 55105, USA
with the assistance of
The Arts Council of Northern Ireland

Printed by The Guernsey Press Company Limited

British Library Cataloguing in Publication Data
Ros, Amanda McKittrick, *1860–1939*
Thine in storm and calm: an Amanda
McKittrick Ros reader
I. Title   II. Ormsby, Frank, *1947*
828'.809

Library of Congress Cataloging-in-Publication Data
Ros, Amanda McKittrick, 1860–1939.
Thine in storm and calm.
Bibliography: p.
1. Ireland—Fiction. 2. Ros, Amanda McKittrick,
1860–1939—Correspondence. 3. Novelists, Irish—20th
century—Correspondence.   I. Ormsby, Frank, 1947–
II. Title.
PR6035.0669A6   1988   823'.912   88–7510
ISBN 0-85640-408-X

CONTENTS

So now I send you on
my book
And through its pages
you can look,
Should you not fully
comprehend
Its lines —
just pass it to a friend.

AMANDA
MCKITTRICK ROS

INTRODUCTION

I

Amanda McKittrick Ros became a celebrity and cult figure almost by accident. Her first novel, *Irene Iddesleigh,* was published in 1897 at the expense of her husband, Andrew Ross, stationmaster at Larne, County Antrim, who paid for the printing as a tenth wedding anniversary gift. Some Irish readers sent a copy to the humorist Barry Pain, who reviewed it in *Black and White* (19 February 1898) as 'The Book of the Century' and brought it to the attention of literary London. As a result, Amanda began to acquire a circle of notable admirers, connoisseurs of the ludicrous in literature, who founded Amanda Ros societies, held dinners at which extracts from her works were read, corresponded with her, and visited her. Among those who admired her work and wrote to and about her over the next sixty years were James Agate, Herbert Henry Asquith, Lord William Henry Beveridge, St John Ervine, Sir Edward Grey, Aldous Huxley, D.B. Wyndham Lewis, E.V. Lucas, Robert Lynd, Desmond MacCarthy, Lord Arthur Ponsonby, Anthony Powell, Siefgried Sassoon, Sir Osbert Sitwell, Sir John Squire, R.H. Tawney and Mark Twain.

Osbert Sitwell, in *Laughter in the Next Room,* attributes the vogue for Amanda to the fact that the literary élite of the time were 'short of a joke', but this is to underestimate the nature of her appeal. Mark Twain, to whom John Horner, a Belfast engineer, had sent a copy of *Irene Iddesleigh*, enthused in a letter to Horner (14 January 1905) that he found it 'enchanting', a worthy rival to the writings of Julia Moore – 'Sweet Singer of Michigan' – in the realms of 'Hogwash' literature. Aldous Huxley, in 'Euphues Redivivus', spoke of Amanda as 'highly prized' by her readers and made a serio-ironic attempt to account for her style. He remarked that the 'first attempts of any people to be consciously literary are always productive of the most elaborate artificiality' and went on to relate Amanda to the euphuists, in that she, like them, was caught up in the 'magical and delicious intoxication' of discovering prose. Many readers shared the intoxication in a way Amanda never intended and perhaps never understood. The unintentional 'enormities' (as Barry Pain called them) of *Irene Iddesleigh, Delina Delaney, Helen Huddleson,* and to a lesser degree *Poems of Puncture* and *Fumes of Formation,* can be merely tedious, but she frequently rises to heights of excess and incongruity which, in both content and style, are irresistibly entertaining.

Huxley felt that the peculiar bent of Amanda's talent was due partly to her isolation from the mainstream. An American critic, Thomas Beer, described her less diplomatically as a 'poor tame woman, wife to a workman, escaping on paper from the knowledge that things had always been dour and plain around her and that they would never be anything else', and it is certainly true that her own accounts of her life, in letters and in conversations with visitors, show a propensity to embellish.

She was born in Drumaness, County Down, on 8 December 1860, the fourth child of Eliza Black and Edward Amlave McKittrick, who was principal of Drumaness High School, and she was christened Anna Margaret at Third Ballynahinch Presbyterian Church on 27 January 1861. However, she told her biographer, Jack Loudan, that her mother had named her after Amanda Malvina Fitzalan, heroine of Regina Maria Roche's novel *Children of the Abbey* (1798) and that her full name (at the time of their conversation) was Amanda Malvina Fitzalan Anna Margaret McLelland McKittrick Ros. Loudan speculates that she dropped the second 's' from her married name 'most likely because she knew that there was a family of ancient lineage called de Ros in County Down'. On other occasions she claimed that the McKittricks were descended from King Sitric of Denmark. In the 1880s she attended Marlborough Teacher Training College in Dublin, was appointed monitor at Millbrook National School, Larne, County Antrim, finished her training at Marlborough, and then became a fully qualified teacher at the same school.

It was on her first trip to Larne that she met Andrew Ross, a widower of thirty-five, who was stationmaster there. She married him at Joymount Presbyterian Church, Carrickfergus, County Antrim, on 30 August 1887. Andrew Ross is, of course, the station agent with the long soft beard, 'whose genial manner and exemplary courteousness are widely known', encountered by Delina Delaney and Lord Gifford on their way to Stranraer; indeed, as Loudan points out, Amanda sends her characters on a totally unnecessary journey so that she may have an opportunity to compliment her husband and to eulogise the man who had helped promote him: E.J. Cotton, general manager of the railway company.

Ross later became stationmaster at Larne Harbour and when Amanda wrote to her confidant T.Stanley Mercer, a bookseller of Thames Ditton, Surrey, about him in 1927, ten years after his death, she felt the need to exaggerate his accomplishments and social success:

> He was a fine English scholar, could speak Russian, French and Norwegian fluently. One day Lord Randolph Churchill caught his arm and they walked arm in arm to the Olderfleet Hotel and dined together. This occurred on every occasion Lord Randolph visited Belfast via Larne and Stranraer.

Visitors were similarly aggrandised. For example, when Desmond MacCarthy called, his companions included an art inspector to the Ministry of Education in Northern Ireland, and a teacher; in a subsequent letter, quoted by Loudan, Amanda refers to the art inspector as the 'Minister for Education in our Northern Parliament' and the teacher as a 'Professor in one of our colleges'.

If her own account is to be believed, Amanda began writing *Irene Iddesleigh* at the age of twelve and finished it between the ages of fourteen and fifteen: 'I locked it up for years, thought no more of it until after I was married, when I drew it forth and remedied some errors and got it printed in 1897' (letter to T.S. Mercer). Whatever the facts, her bulky second novel, *Delina Delaney*, was ready for publication the following year. In addition to a preface attacking Barry Pain's review of *Irene Iddesleigh*, the new work incorporated a number of attacks on critics, prompted by Pain's comments and by those of others; these outbursts introduced a note of anger and vituperation that was to pervade Amanda's writings for the rest of her life.

3

Critics were not the only target. In 1907 Amanda undertook the management of a lime kiln and farm at Glenoe, near Larne, the property of a friend of her husband named Crawford, who was ill. Some of Crawford's relations and neighbours resented her managerial style, and a bitter battle ensued which hardened her already well-developed hostility towards solicitors. For years she poured her energies into a novel called 'Six Months in Hell', never finished, intended as a denunciation of the legal profession. Her rage did find immediate outlet, however, in *Poems of Puncture* (1912) and rumbled also through *Fumes of Formation* (1933), and *Helen Huddleson* (1969), the novel published thirty years after her death with a concluding chapter by Jack Loudan.

Andrew Ross died in 1917 and Amanda, having had two ground-floor rooms of her house, Iddesleigh, converted into a drapery store and a grocery, spent several years quarrelling with customers over the payment of bills, and with a confectioner to whom she had rented one of the shops over Sunday opening. She then abandoned commerce and on 12 June 1922 she married Thomas Rodgers of Clintnagooland, near Ballynahinch, County Down, and went to live there. During this period, the Nonesuch Press edition of *Irene Iddesleigh* appeared – an event which Amanda regarded as her proper elevation to the 'shelf of Classic' – and she wrote 'St Scandalbags', her riposte to Wyndham Lewis's review of the edition. She was also moved to exultant verse by the death of Barry Pain.

Widowed again in 1933, she returned to Iddesleigh a few years later and embarked upon a further series of squabbles with tradesmen and solicitors. She went into hospital early in 1939, having fractured her thigh in a fall, and died there on 3 February, some three months after her seventy-eighth birthday and some three years after she had written to her Belfast friend Norman Carrothers,

> I am back in the old house once more and shall be until the Master calls me home and places me in a kindly nook of his vast mansions, but indeed if I get slipped into a small snug bungalow where there will be plenty of ink – a pen – and writing pads, I will be content.

'My works are all expressly my own, pleasingly peculiar, not a borrowed stroke in one of them', Amanda wrote in a letter to T.S. Mercer. Pleasingly peculiar they are, but the claim to originality is an exaggeration: her novels are peopled with innocent maidens whose virtue is threatened, with honest country folk, scheming villains, faithful retainers; there are elopements, betrayals, disasters, coincidences, separations, reunions; there are sparkling jewels, lavish costumes, ornate interiors; vulnerable virtue and lurid corruption are in constant opposition and there is much moralising; the pace is often frenetic, the atmosphere feverish. If these works are Amanda's own, they are so chiefly in the incongruous lengths to which she carries certain traditional features of romantic fiction.

The bodies of Amanda's characters, for example, labour spectacularly, and sometimes indelicately, to register emotional turmoil. It is not enough that bosoms heave, lips tremble, flushes mount; that hands are clammy, feet are stamped, voices quiver; that faces grow wan, pallid, ashen, and haggard, and that eyes drown in tears. In *Delina Delaney* we are told that the blood of Madam-de-Maine 'boiled to overflowing as she thickly smutted her cambric handkerchief with its carmine stain'. At other points she bites her lip, 'provoking its bloody flow with pleasurable exertion', stands 'spuing with venom', and feels every nerve in her body 'dance to the quivering tune of her bloody pores'. Lady Gifford, in the same novel, tosses her 'haughty head as high as she reasonably could without pain' and clears her throat of 'any little mucus that perchance would serve to obstruct the tone of her resolute explanation'. Lord Gifford's frame shakes 'as if electrically tampered with' and he sheds 'globules of liquid lava'. Indeed, perspiration is produced by the gallon: during the ball at Dilworth Castle, for instance, the heat is 'too oppressive to allow much comfort to the corpulent' (*Irene Iddesleigh*); Maurice Munro's brow 'was pebbled with perspiration dropped thither by the joyful fingers of intense feelings' (*Helen Huddleson*); and the servant Susan Sylvester is a 'mass of moist anxiety' (*Helen Huddleson*).

Physical illness is described even more graphically:

> Lord Gifford's proud face looked ashy dead, as he lay on his great and elegant bed. His eyes had lost their stupid look and bloodshot trimming and assumed a stare of wildness; his thin hands seemed gloved in colourless hose streaked with veiny indigo; and whilst the doctor examined the wounds on his face, the lips of which were red and swollen, he kept wringing them in apparent agony.

Amanda follows this description with the bathetic splendour of:

> 'I fear you are not so well today, Lord Gifford,' the doctor remarked gravely.

There are numerous such examples of novelistic conventions being stretched and shattered. Madam-de-Maine is recognisable as a stock villainess, but what stock villainess ever committed murder and then hummed an eight-line song, apparently composed on the spot, over the body of her victim? And when did disaster strike with such decisive frequency as in the family of Helen Potter? Her younger brother shoots Mrs Potter by accident and strangles himself immediately afterwards; Mr Potter becomes 'berthed in the boat of insanity', dying three months later. One might cite also the alliterative excesses to be found on almost every page of Amanda's novels, the torrential loquacity and preposterous eloquence of her characters, especially when angry or grief-stricken, and the relentless embellishment of the mundane – legs become 'bony supports', Sundays are 'sanctified measures of time', eyes are 'globes of glare' and 'human spectacles', a train moves by 'steamy endeavour' – as further evidence of how she appropriates in a characteristic way the conventions of this type of prose fiction.

Another pleasing peculiarity of Amanda's prose is her idiosyncratic use and misuse of particular words. In *Delina Delaney* she favours the verb 'to sister': Madam-de-Maine would 'jealously fling a look of fire, sistered with a silent curse'; 'at the end of five weeks Delina sistered consciousness'; and Modesty Manor (in *Helen Huddleson*) contains mirrors 'framed in priceless massiveness sistered with scenery'. Again, the words 'north' and 'south' are applied to the body a number of times: the statue of Lord

Gifford's father has a 'bald north', and Maurice Munro thanks Helen Potter not from the bottom of his heart but from 'the south of this, the tenderest trait within my trunk of torture'. In *Poems of Puncture* the Reverend Goliath Ginbottle's 'forehead is flat but no matter for that/On its south are two hairbrushes turned up on end', and Billy Doherty (in *Helen Huddleson*) turned his eyes 'north' to Maurice Munro. In 'St Scandalbags' trousers are referred to as a 'southern necessary'.

Amanda also uses words inaccurately or in a curiously off-focus way: Lady Gifford is a 'high-bred daughter of distinguished effeminacy'; Madam-de-Maine is an 'incendious woman'; and the prison caretaker, Roderic Dalrymple (in *Delina Delaney*), at one time 'enjoyed the covetous reputation of being placed on the list of grammar school teachers'. More disconcerting in its effect, perhaps, is her use of 'socialism' to refer to upper-class society, a wealthy élite: the castle of Lord and Lady Dilworth is a 'heightened haunt of high-born socialism'; Sir John Dunfern finds it 'almost impossible to stare socialism in the face' (that is, he dislikes social gatherings of his own class); Irene Iddesleigh was once the 'envied object of socialism'; and Billy Doherty refers to 'all the aristocratic bigwigs and socialists in the country'. *Helen Huddleson,* in particular, contains numerous coinages formed with the suffix '-dom': damndom, devildom, monkdom, straydom, seekdom, priestdom, gospeldom, youthdom, fooldom, bastardom.

Another source of unintended humour in Amanda's work is the prevalence of the misrelated participle. Here Irene Iddesleigh knocks at the door of Audley Hall: 'Knocking loudly twice before any attempt was made to open the door, there came at last an aged man with halting step and shaking limb.' 'Partaking heartily of a well-cooked supper,' we are told, 'sleep soon found purchasers in Lord Gifford and Delina Delaney.' *Helen Huddleson* is particularly rich in examples. Lord Raspberry embraces Helen: 'Eagerly endeavouring to get away, he held her still closer to him.' Lord Raspberry encounters Porter Jamie at a railway station: 'Grasping a truck and wheeling it hurriedly away, Lord Raspberry exclaimed "Halloo", and the porter returning, he placed a sovereign in his hand.' Lord Raspberry is angry with Madam Pear: 'Stamping his foot, Madam Pear listened aghast as he went on. . .' Helen

Huddleson prepares to leave Father Guerdo's gate lodge: 'Putting on her little sailor hat, Father Guerdo stood facing the rustic ruby. . .'

Yet another characteristic form of expression is to be found in phrases such as 'the jeering laugh that bespake the heartless heart', 'a picture of lifeless life', 'against her wished-for wish'.

Such itemising does not convey Amanda's gift for startling the reader with sudden extravagances and felicities of expression. 'Only another week and I shall almost cease to be a free thinker,' muses Irene Iddesleigh as her wedding day approaches. Delina Delaney and Lord Gifford are ushered into a kitchen behind a bar by the proprietress, 'with a maximum peasant grace'. A sigh, 'memorable for its trembling and broken depth', escapes from Lord Gifford, and Maurice Munro tells Helen Potter that 'on receiving the letter from Mabel Moag, thronged became my mind with thoughts the thorniest'. As Lord Raspberry enters the Spa Hotel in Ballynahinch 'an empty ventricle [reminds] him that his entrails [seem] badly neglected'. Here is Lord Gifford, faced with a two-hour wait for a train: 'Longing for the surrender of a cigar to his lifey lips of action, [he] was soon seen destroying, by a necessary destructive, the butt-end of one.' And Helen Huddleson's Atlantic voyage is recorded in a single, memorable sentence: 'They reached Canada after a very pleasant trip across the useful pond that stimulates the backbone of commerce more than any other known element since Noah, captain of the flood, kicked the bucket.' Any reader might compile a much-extended list.

Certain themes run aggressively through all Amanda's novels. One is a hatred of alcohol. Drink drives Irene Iddlesleigh's mother to shoot her husband. It is the 'powerful monster of mangled might' that contributes to Oscar Otwell's ruination and suicide. The description in *Delina Delaney* of the gin shop and its frequenters resembles the most lurid of temperance-movement pamphlets and Lord Gifford's descent into dipsomania not only destroys his health and spirit but leaves him vulnerable to the machinations of Madam-de-Maine. *Delina Delaney* and *Helen Huddelson* are further enlivened by Amanda's hatred of critics and lawyers – her fame was due in considerable measure to these animosities – and her disapproval of most clergymen. The Bishop of Barelegs, who officiates at Irene Iddesleigh's wedding, for example, is clearly named with satirical intent, as is Mr Luther Alfred Sydney Knox Windrim West Varley, rector of the Church of St Assumption, in *Delina Delaney*. Her attitudes in these matters are predictable and unchanging. Only in her response to Catholicism is there a traceable progression – or regression – as sympathy and mild satire are poisoned by distrust and bigotry.

The heroine of *Delina Delaney* is Catholic and she and her family are presented as decent and virtuous, though superstitious. If there is bigotry here, it is latent, more patronising than virulent, like the distinction Amanda makes between the clarity of Northern Irish pronunciation and the 'wild provincialisms prevalent among the West and South of Ireland's inhabitants'. The portrayal of the mercenary and hypocritical Father O'Malley, who offers up prayers at the funeral of Mrs Delaney 'in a very buttermilk fashion' and exploits Catholic fears of purgatory, is sharper but not especially anti-Catholic; he is merely one of the 'men of every Gospel standing' who have little concern for the welfare of their flocks.

Helen Huddleson (the unfinished novel on which Amanda seems to have worked sporadically during the 1920s) is, however, often bitterly anti-Catholic, as though the Home Rule crisis and the establishment of Northern Ireland as a separate state had galvanised her already muscular Presbyterianism, in the way that her dealings with critics and lawyers had stirred her aggression generally. This change of mood may be indicated by her references to Dublin: in *Delina Delaney* it is 'Ireland's antique metropolis. . . [a] lovely city'; by the time she wrote *Helen Huddleson* it had become the 'city of bigotry. . . [the] city of wanton bloodshed. . . [the] Irish metropolis of Protestant mistrust'. Rome is, more drastically, 'that zone of idolatry and bigotry. . . whose rankness is fast decaying under the influential and potent power of Protestantism' and Lord Raspberry's sister, Cherry Raspberry, dreams that she has died and gone to heaven 'despite the evil invented objectives of popery against Protestants'. Father Guerdo, the disgraced priest who acts as keeper of the gate lodge at the

Convent of St Iscariot and is a victim of the 'professional routine which Roman tyranny imposes on her sons of heresy, mockery and idolatry', associates clandestinely with several of the nuns and represents a challenge to Helen's Presbyterianism. The influence of the great Reverend John Davis DD, of the Third Ballynahinch Presbyterian Church, prevails, and she refuses to call Guerdo 'Father'. Guerdo himself undergoes a sudden conversion:

> 'I now cast aside for ever the imaginative flames of purgatory, that false dogma that popery advocates. Yes, yes, in future I relinquish all those farces of religion I was forced to swallow with a throat of sincerity plaguing my brain's tiny inlets to admit such heathenish devilology.'

This is the Amanda who wrote two (unpublished) attacks on popery entitled 'To Cardinal MacRory, RC' and 'Stripping Christ to Clothe Peter', whose letters to Norman Carrothers in the 1930s were sometimes headed 'No Pope', and who could lambast a local clergyman for having failed to prevent the marriage of a young Protestant woman to a Catholic.

Expressions of anger and prejudice, the settling of scores in *Delina Delaney* and *Helen Huddleson,* contribute to the comparative diffuseness of these novels. Structurally they are not so controlled as *Irene Iddesleigh*. As Loudan points out, the characters in the two later novels are considerably more garrulous than those in the first and this too makes for diffuseness, especially in *Delina Delaney,* which runs to some 100,000 words. It seems that Amanda did have the impulse to experiment with other techniques: *Helen Huddleson* begins in the present and moves back into the past, and 'Six Months in Hell', as its title suggests, is ambitious in intention, but her energies were deflected into other channels, largely negative or self-defensive. For this, the very critics who helped to establish her 'reputation' bear some of the responsibility.

3

Amanda's war against the critics began in earnest the day she read Barry Pain's review of *Irene Iddesleigh* and was waged in novels, poems, correspondence, and unpublished writings until her death in 1939. In *Bayonets of Bastard Sheen* (1949) T.S. Mercer published a selection of her letters to him on the subject and included an alphabetical list of fifty epithets that she had applied at various times to critics, who are, for example, 'bastard donkey-headed mites', 'clay-crabs of corruption', 'denunciating Arabs', 'egotistical earthworms', 'evil-minded snapshots of spleen', and 'talent-wipers of a wormy order'. The two chief skirmishes in this forty years' war were with Barry Pain, for his review of *Irene Iddesleigh*, and with D.B. Wyndham Lewis for his review of the Nonesuch Press edition of the same novel (*Daily Mail*, 17 November 1926).

Barry Pain's review title – 'The Book of the Century' – and opening sentences establish the tone of his article:

> Last year, at what precise time I know not, possibly we were wrapped in sleep, and had no notion that any great tragedy was happening – last year, then, more or less and at the price of half a crown, and printed at Belfast by W.E.G. Baird, Ltd, who were also of London, not to mention Dublin, appeared *Irene Iddesleigh* by Mrs Amanda McKittrick Ros. That is a long and rocky sentence, but if you go slowly at it and worry it, you will find that it has a meaning. That is one of the principal respects in which it differs from *Irene Iddesleigh* by Mrs Amanda McKittrick Ros.

He finds that though the book amused him at first, its 'enormities' became so overwhelming that he 'shrank before it in tears and terror'. He quotes some 'reflections' to illustrate the 'full beauty' of the style and comments that the novel 'is a thing that happens once in a million years. There is no one above it, and no one beside it, and it sits alone as the nightingale sings.' He goes on to identify its 'most stupendous and monumental characteristic' as its 'absence of any sense of humour' and concludes that criticism is impotent in the face of such 'dazzling' achievement.

Amanda's reply takes the form of an 8000-word preface to *Delina Delaney*, in which she sets about her enemy with ponderous irony. He is a 'colossal, gigantic, awe-inspiring, thrilling critic of worldwide fame. . . [the] so-called Barry Pain. . . this Himalayan critic'. His 'penning powers [are] terrific as the crashing sound of a burst soap-bubble'. She comments on every sentence in the review and adapts some of the reviewer's own phrases against him: 'he sits alone, indeed, or, rather, stands alone, as the donkey brays'. She apologises for her audacity in publishing a novel without consulting him, answers his reference to lack of meaning by offering to lend him a 'net some day that will land [him] unto the coast of conception', and chides Irene for having teased, then rebuffed, the critic: 'Why had you not the kindly courage to caress the keen trait of brute fondness you at first aroused and dare its dwindling again into trembling nothing?' The review, she maintains, has had no effect on the novel's popularity:

> Irene is admired. . . as on that night, that memorable night, on which she bit Barry so severely underneath the blankets with her teeth of unfathomable fanginess, infusing their poisonous saliva so strongly throughout his pores of retention, that ease was only procured by lashing the result, in its most fangy nature, on a page of Black and White (249) of 19 February 1898, and withal, I say, notwithstanding this bilious effusion, Irene continues, as before, to still gain favour with her many aristocratic admirers.

Pain's contention that *Irene Iddesleigh* is 'on a scale that has never before been attempted', is hailed as a 'perfectly just statement'; it is this stupendous scale that has 'irritated Barry's monotonous disease, turning it into a cancerous irritant wart, that shall spread and twine its branches of deadly sting so firmly around the heart of defeat as to shut the hand that dared to strike a blighting blow'.

Little wonder that Wyndham Lewis approaches the Nonesuch Press edition of the novel with mock trepidation: 'One has to be careful about this fine book. Some years ago. . . Mr Barry Pain allowed his joy to get the better of his discretion and retribution was swift.' So instead of directly criticising the moment in the novel when Sir John implores Irene to say whether she has been deceitful and hypocritical, Lewis comments on the illustration by W.M.R. Quick which depicts Sir John's 'agony':

> I see from the illustration that in his agony Sir John has allowed his trousers to sag. One hand is clutching his whiskers, the other grasps the back of a plush armchair. I presume that he has been tearing wildly at his braces. In the year 1897, recollect, Baronets wore their trousers baggy. Sir John's are simply incredible.
>
> *Reflection*: Perhaps his wife grew cold to him on this account.

Lewis comments in a similar vein on the 'dastardly' nature of Sir John's trousers in another of the illustrations, combines a resumé of the plot with sketches of the main characters, then returns to the subject of trousers: 'My personal feeling is that Oscar [Otwell], though a drunkard and wife-beater, *pressed his trousers under the bed*, and was for that reason irresistible to every woman who beheld him.' He speculates further about trousers as a 'deciding factor in the home and foreign policy of the Victorians' and implies that Disraeli's influence with Queen Victoria derived from the 'smooth and flowing' quality of his 'canary trousers'.

Amanda retaliated by nicknaming Lewis 'St Scandalbags' and writing a 10,000-word diatribe in which she brands the *Daily Mail* a 'celestial-like-celebrated-talent-tarnisher' and Lewis a 'criticising crowdrop' whose 'blackguardly insinuations against the character of our late ever-lamented Queen Victoria in conjunction with one of our Parliamentary Pillars of Politics [are] hellish'.

One year later her anger was stirred again when an American edition of the novel appeared. The anger was directed firstly at the publishers, Boni and Liveright, who had, through a misunderstanding with the Nonesuch Press, issued the book without her permission; even when the matter had been explained and royalties paid, she was implacable, describing American publishers, in letters to T.S. Mercer, as a 'gang of thieves. . . a mean, snivelling lot of bombastic egotism'. She turned also on the Nonesuch Press, blaming them for the confusions that had arisen and demanding compensation – but her most outraged reaction of all was against Thomas Beer, who in his introduction to the edition described her as a Belfast housewife attempting to escape from a 'dour and plain' existence. Loudan records that she tore the introduction from the book and sent it to T.S. Mercer, together with a letter extolling the wealth, talent, and social status of her family and relatives and adding the word 'bastard' before Beer's name. She also composed an eighty-eight line poem, 'Reply of Author to Tommy Beer's Critique on *Irene Iddesleigh*', in which Beer is reviled as an 'empty gasbag', accused of jealousy and spite, addressed as 'braggy, swaggy, Yankee Tom' and described as a 'lying critic cad':

The novelist who *Irene* wrote
'The Belfast wife' – Tom Beer to quote,
I contradict his filthy lie
And will until the day I die.
Those Belfast wives are better far
Than those of other nations are;
Unlike the dandy Yankee breed
Their children are their husbands' seed.

Later she made reference in *Helen Huddleson* to a 'buddy called Beer, an ould scandaliser of books, no matther 'twas the Holy Bible, he'd hev somethin' dhirty til say even about *it*' and to 'Lewis (another windy yapp that snarls and barks)'.

There are a number of such salvoes in the novels and poems published after *Irene Iddesleigh*. At an emotional high point in *Delina Delaney*, Lord Gifford picks up a magazine which contains a review of a novel by his cousin May Marchmont and immediately goes on the attack. Some time afterwards, while he and Delina wait for a train at York Road terminus, Belfast, Gifford throws a cigar butt to the ground, which is 'instantly picked up by a stout-lunged newsboy or beggar editor of a penny birdie weekly'. Amanda is here taking revenge on the editor of a Belfast periodical, the *Magpie*, in which a reviewer had remarked that '[The editor] has asked me to mention that *Irene Iddesleigh* is a novel by Mrs Amanda Ros: and that it can be recommended as an antidote for a dull Sunday, but as to what it is all about, God alone Knoweth, for the *Magpie* staff hath given it up.' And in *Helen Huddleson*, Snowdrop Lodge has been 'untenanted since the death of Lady Dolly Dray. . . the novelist whose fat resources were diminished by the scurrilous, scandalising, spiteful critic scions of bastardom, found always trampling upon the heels of fame'.

One other assault on critics should be mentioned here. In 1954 T.S. Mercer's Merle Press published *Donald Dudley, The Bastard Critic*, an early version of the first episode of Amanda's projected novel, 'Six Months in Hell', and the only portion of that work to appear in print. Dudley is a 'poor, ragged, hungry mortal', what the 'good folk north of Ireland's verdant diameter term. . . a thorough bandy-legged work of creation', who is employed by unscrupulous editors as a 'slasher' of literary genius. He lodges in abject squalor with Miss Shorthorn, one of 'that class who subsist on the prostitute penny', constantly cursing his mother for 'blighting her chastity and bowing in filthy fashion before a voluptuous viper of pulpit importance', the Reverend Donald Dudley, to 'satiate the beastly lust that lurked in his treacherous, immoral heart'. His meagre earnings as a scorner of talented authors favoured by the public are augmented by chopping wood, mending half-worn boots thrown his way by charitable suburbanites, and 'in extreme cases of absolute necessity, black boots for "fast women" and a few papery fops always to be found loitering adjacent to the General Post Office'. He has a conversation with a mysterious Mr Devildinger, in which they discuss, among other subjects, the superior qualities of the novelist Addy Rivers. Dudley suffers the humiliations Amanda would have liked to inflict on all critics, that '"gather-up" of boasty nothings', those 'illiterate tooters', 'rotten columns. . . expressive only of a clique of "corner-boy dross" or "jarvey-wags"'.

The death of Barry Pain (1928) was cause for celebration: Amanda wrote a chirpy letter to T.S. Mercer – 'So old Barry Pain is gone – I don't feel sorry – his worldly wealth only reaching something like £1623!!!' – and composed her poem 'The End of "Pain"'. He is, of course, consigned to hell, the destination for all those whom Amanda most disapproved of – critics, lawyers, American publishers, editors, corrupt clerics, the intemperate, Kaiser Bill, and women who wore trousers.

4

In *Poems of Puncture*, the first of her two collections of verse, Amanda occasionally celebrates such qualities as charity, truth, kindness, and love. There are didactic narratives such as 'The Old Windmill', in which Lord Lightheart pretends to be a beggar in order to test the love of a woman (her virtue triumphs and she becomes Lady Lightheart), and 'Fanny Malone', whose heroine refuses to help Major Mat Munro, who then freezes to death. 'The

Old Home' and 'The Old Chestnut' are as mawkishly nostalgic as their titles suggest and in 'Rover', an effusion about a good-natured dog, the creature is admired for a willingness to forgive that Amanda finds lamentably lacking in human beings.

Such poems are merely lulls in a spectacular storm of invective. Amanda is out to 'puncture', to deflate her enemies – and they are legion. The town of Tare, in the poem of that name, is a microcosm of the corruption she sees everywhere: she approves of some of its citizens but on the whole it is a lesser Pandemonium, riddled with lewdness, filth, debased clergymen, unscrupulous, foul-mouthed doctors, unsatisfactory teachers and tradesmen, misers, vain spinsters, and assorted miscreants:

> . . .that devil-despiser Lundy,
> Who wouldn't eat eggs that were laid on a Sunday,
> And Crabby Macfluster of Windy Mount
> Who follows women in endless count.

But it is the lawyers in particular – 'the greatest of all living hounds' – who are subjected to the most virulent and sustained abuse. Amanda herself was incurably litigious and frequently the subject of litigation, and her letters reveal that for most of her life she considered herself victimised and exploited by members of the profession. It is no surprise to find her writing to T.S. Mercer in 1928: 'Re *Poems of Puncture* – I wrote them as filthy debt to dishonest lawyers'; indeed at the time the poems were published, she was at work on the unfinished novel 'Six Months in Hell', which was, as she informed another correspondent, 'written chiefly to cut up the lawyers, a gang I absolutely detest'. One suspects that Amanda incorporated material from this work in *Helen Huddleson*, where lawyers are reviled no fewer than eight times. The hall of Crow Cottage, for instance, is decorated with wooden gargoyles representing 'liars, in other words, lawyers'; Maurice Munro reads to Helen Potter a description by the novelist Agra Raymond's of the revolting 'Barney Bloater KC' and praises Agra for her scathing treatment of the legal profession; he also tells Helen the story of how the avaricious Simon Swag swindled his servant Almina Rowley.

The seven direct attacks in *Poems of Puncture* are entitled: 'A

Limb of Law'; 'Micky Monkeyface McBlear'; 'The Ugliest Brute in Britain'; 'Jamie Jarr'; 'Epitaph on Largebones – the Lawyer'; 'Lawyer Jock'; and 'Po – the Lawyer'. All the victims are caricatured as physically unprepossessing, brutish and greedy: Geordie in 'A Limb of Law' has a 'horrid, hairless crown':

> His huge white tusks were false ones, to match the wig he wore,
> His heart was likewise ditto – deception to the core.

He is cunning and pompous, and when he dies, he joins the 'regiment of legal rascals' in hell. The concluding lines are mildly scatological:

> For never will a lawbum roost on Heaven's rung
> To dirty on the saints below – Ding-Dong-Dung!

The lawyer Bullyrag in 'The Ugliest Brute in Britain' resembles a mare, pig, goat, and stoat.

> His neck is long and rummy yellow, which helps to lengthen this
>   base fellow,
> His lugs are large and lie in line with a snout that God forbid
>   'twas mine.
> His head, shaped like a rotten pear, has bumps stuck round it
>   here and there,
> Stuffed with muddy brains and batter with a slit in front, whence
>   oozes clatter.

He will join his friend Micky Monkeyface McBlear, who already 'shovels coke to the Reverend Bloke'. When Amanda's enemies died – whether they were lawyers, or critics, or involved in legal wrangles with her, like Sapphira Slick, the subject of another piece in *Poems of Puncture* – her epitaphs for them tended to be a form of gloating at the graveside.

At one point in the collection Amanda genially wishes us 'A silver pipe to smoke quite handy,/A copper flask well filled with brandy', but warns immediately that we are not to allow them to make us 'unruly': intemperance is as much a target in *Poems of Puncture* as it is in her novels. 'To Those Whom the Shoe Fits' takes as its subject drunken women and the degradation into which alcohol leads those 'bipeds so inclined'. The poem shows considerable moral confusion: on the one hand, the 'Christians of the city' are encouraged to treat such women with kindness and strive for their salvation; on the other, Amanda recommends that 'Such intoxicating drabbies/Should be tied to a stake,/Their buttocks whipped with fishing-hooks,/Then frizzled on the grate.' The Reverend Goliath Ginbottle is, presumably, another inebriate, though Amanda contents herself with ridiculing his appearance, hypocrisy, domestic tyranny, and lack of Christianity, and looks forward to dancing in heaven to celebrate his damnation.

Poems of Puncture is as often repellent as it is amusing but has a unifying splenetic vigour; *Fumes of Formation,* the last of Amanda's books to be published during her lifetime, is by comparison subdued. 'This inventive production was hatched within a mind fringed with *Fumes of Formation,* the ingenious innings of inspiration and Thorny Tincture of Thought', the epigraph promises, but the epigraph is more memorable than the bulk of the contents.

The book includes further attacks on 'legal hounds' and critics, but with the exception of 'The End of "Pain"' and 'Epitaph Suitable for a Critic's Tomb' they seem almost automatic. The most spirited poems are those in which Amanda addresses herself to what she saw as a decline in moral standards among women: 'The Old Home' (not to be confused with a poem of the same name in *Poems of Puncture*) laments the subversion of Victorian morality by the introduction of trousers for women; powder and paint are denounced in 'Days of Decency – Dead' and 'Opinion Rules the World' (in the latter, women who smoke, curse, spit, and wear their hair short are designated 'dirty clarts'); and in 'My Betrothed' the 'practically sound' woman described possesses 'the sweetest mouth e'er made,/Void of that horrid smell/of cigs. . .' Kaiser Wilhelm is another target: in 'On E. of G.' Amanda's God proves as formidable and malicious as herself:

> He found when you were being formed
> 'Twere better you were singly armed.

And one wonders whether the 'digit of dollardom, USA' who asked her to write a few lines in a copy of *Irene Iddesleigh,* or the 'dispenser of spiritual foppery' who asked her to 'pour' from one of her 'tiny brain-cells a little drop of poetry, instantly and original, allowing five minutes for composition', or the 'Grandee' who sought an opinion on his 'efforts as a Poet' were chastened or secretly delighted by the brief insulting verses she provided.

Outside such flashes of disgust and impatience, the sustained inanity of 'A Soldier's Missive', and some poems in a nostalgic and sentimental vein similar to that found in *Poems of Puncture*, it is fair to say that in *Fumes of Formation* Amanda is much preoccupied with Death and Judgment. In addition to numerous epitaphs and elegies there are several sick-bed and deathbed melodramas: in 'Barbara Bligh Black' the sick girl asks her visitor to smooth the pillow 'once again like what thou didst before' and talks of the day she will have a 'sheet of moss around [her] and a sod upon [her] head'; little Jacob Jay, dying on his fifth birthday, promises to meet his mother again one day on 'God's Lawn'.

The poem 'Thoughts' may be taken as representative of the dominant mood: the speaker visits a cemetery with pen and paper – 'No place I love to visit more/Than tracks of lifeless friends' – meditates on the common fate of the evil and the virtuous, the rich and the poor, and speculates on Judgment Day:

> What if the poor the rich shall be
> Before poor Riches' eyes!!!

'Death's Silent Symbol', an address to the death-robe that will 'shield' and clasp the speaker and share her corruption, ends with a similarly hopeful reference to the day they will 'dodge the damp and damn dismay'.

Amanda published at least three poems in broadsheet form: the elegy 'In Memory of the late Edward J. Cotton, Esq., General Manager of the Belfast and Northern Counties Railway, Ireland' (*c.* 1899), 'Kaiser Bill!' (*c.* 1915), and 'A Little Belgian Orphan' (1916), signed pseudonymously 'Monica Moyland' and inspired by the presence of Belgian refugees in the Larne area. I have reprinted the latter for its rarity value and because it is representative of a type of verse popular at the time. The best of the other poems among her papers is 'The Engineer Divine', written on the evening of Andrew Ross's funeral (1917): it is the most sustained example of the train and railway imagery common in her writings and oddly effective as an elegy, perhaps because of the feeling which reverberates under the extended metaphor.

In Osbert Sitwell's *Laughter in the Next Room* (1949) he recalls a conversation in Harold Munro's Poetry Bookshop with a young Anglo-Italian writer:

> His name, we will say, was Giorgio di Dragoni. He proceeded to relate to me how he had entered into a correspondence with Amanda McKittrick Ros. . . He had hoped to draw her out. But when he had written to her, telling her how much he liked her novel, instead of receiving the amiable reply he had expected, he found in its very first lines a memorable snub – 'Dear Mr Giorgio di Dragoni,' it began, 'your name – if such it can be called – is unfamiliar to me.'

Until *Irene Iddesleigh* attained the 'shelf of Classic', Amanda's publications could be ordered only from herself, so she had many correspondents. Furthermore, admirers like 'Giorgio di Dragoni' often wrote to her in the hope that she would reply in the vein they admired. Her reactions were unpredictable. 'Always at Home to the Honourable', her visiting card proclaimed, and letters from the Honourable were equally welcome: she was likely to respond seriously to a Captain Whalley or a Richard Denman MP; others could suffer the fate of those who asked for instant poems or inscriptions and be subjected to insult or Olympian disdain. This may have been a defensive stratagem, the outcome of a suspicion that not all the admiration expressed in letters was genuine. When she decided that certain correspondents were teasing her or when her natural spikiness was provoked, her reaction sometimes took the form of spontaneous jottings on the offending letters; one from a Dorset reader, who wrote to Amanda in 1911 employing some of her own mannerisms, has the comment, 'What an alliterative bloody ass!'

Amanda's most sustained correspondence was with T. S. Mercer, who had discovered her work in the 1920s. When he first wrote to her in 1927, she was in a rage over Thomas Beer's introduction to *Irene Iddesleigh* and seems to have turned to this new admirer as a sympathetic confidant. They corresponded regularly for ten years, during which time Amanda sent Mercer numerous drafts of her works-in-progress (he refers, for example, to portions of fourteen versions of 'Six Months in Hell' and to four versions of 'St Scandalbags'), and he typed some manuscripts for her. Many of her letters to him are on the subject of critics. After her death, he published a selection of these letters under the title *Bayonets of Bastard Sheen* (1949) and in 1954 he issued editions of 'St Scandalbags' and *Donald Dudley, The Bastard Critic*, an early fragment of 'Six Months in Hell'. When his large collection of Rosiana was sold by the Guildhall Bookshop, Twickenham, in 1973, it contained numerous manuscripts of the published novels and books of poems, fragments of abortive works, as well as the unpublished attacks on popery, unpublished poems, and a selection of books which referred to her and her work.

Other valued advisers were Norman Carrothers, and John Coghlan, a Dubliner, a 'very decent person and quite alone in the World. . . extremely well educated', one who 'suits the art of corresponding'. Coghlan sent her his stories and poems for her opinion, read the manuscript of *Helen Huddleson* and suggested revisions, arranged for the publication of six of her poems in the *London Mercury* (January 1933) and at one point was to have been her literary executor. Loudan tells us that Amanda's trinket box contained, oddly, Robert Emmet's speech from the dock during his trial, a withered pea pod that Andrew Ross had eaten the peas from on his deathbed, and copies of Coghlan's poems.

If Amanda put her enemies in her books, she did not forget her friends. The Chatto & Windus edition of *Delina Delaney* is dedicated to John Coghlan; Helen Huddleson travels to Canada in a ship under the command of Captain Carrothers, and the comatose Lord Raspberry is attended by Doctor Stanley Mercer, a 'physician of exceptional promise'. Doctor Mercer's fellow physician Professor Tillard takes his name from Philip Tillard, the teacher who visited Amanda in the company of MacCarthy, Carrothers and John Hunter. Coghlan, Mercer and Carrothers join Amanda's 'company of the approved', with Aldous Huxley, the Reverend John Davis DD, of Third Ballynahinch Presbytertian Church, and Doctor Frances Neil, 'a lady unsurpassed for her professional skill and enormously successful with her overflowing list of patients, rarely if ever courting defeat in one case out of a thousand'.

6

This anthology began in delight some years ago when I first read *Irene Iddesleigh, Delina Delaney* and *Helen Huddleson*. An extended acquaintance with Amanda's life and work has prompted more ambivalent reactions, among them unease. It is not simply the guilt one might feel about an enterprise that the author herself, were she alive, would certainly disapprove of and that she might well find hurtful, but a troubling sense of creative impulses and energies gone awry. It would be an exaggeration to suggest that Amanda was a great, or even a good, novelist *manquée*, yet to read her is to be haunted by a sense of authentic frustrated pressures struggling for outlet and to wonder what, in different circumstances, she might have produced.

Other readers have been similarly troubled. 'She cannot be altogether laughed off,' wrote Anthony Powell; 'she may be a long way from Shakespeare, but she partakes, in however infinitely minute a degree, of the Shakespearean power over language.' James Agate described her as 'an artist, if a mistaken one' with a 'rich and joyous sense of words' that many 'reputable' novelists lacked.

Such comparisons and matters for speculation aside, it is finally Amanda's power to delight – however unintentionally – that makes her work still worth reading. She had indeed for decades 'disturbed the bowels' of her readers in ways she never suspected and the best of her work is no less startling now than when it acquired its first devotees. 'I expect I will be talked about at the end of 1000 years,' she wrote. Perhaps she was right.

Frank Ormsby
Belfast
July 1988

from
FUMES OF FORMATION

ON VISITING WESTMINSTER ABBEY
A 'REDUCED DIGNITY' INVITED ME
TO MUSE ON ITS MERITS

Holy Moses! Have a look!
Flesh decayed in every nook!
Some rare bits of brain lie here,
Mortal loads of beef and beer,
Some of whom are turned to dust,
Every one bids lost to lust;
Royal flesh so tinged with 'blue'
Undergoes the same as you.
Wealth and lands were theirs to boast,
Yachts lying nigh to every coast,
Homage from the million theirs
Clad in gold and gorgeous wares.
Here they lie who had such store,
Move a muscle – nevermore;
Dead as all before them died:
Richer man are you beside,
Begging as you walk your way,
Life still yours while dead are they:
All the refuse lying here
Has no life to give it cheer.
Alas! You stand above them all
Tho' poverty did you befall.
Life was thine, once noble lord!
Now you tramp on their record.
Tributes of 'Masonic Love'
Shall not passports prove Above.
Slabs of monumental art
Tell the sycophants' remarks.
Noble once, these dead folk now,
Darkness stamped have on their brow.
All portrays without – within
Lots of love and shoals of sin.

Famous some were — yet they died:
Poets — Statesmen — Rogues beside,
Kings — Queens, all of them do rot,
What about them? Now — they're not!

A SOLDIER'S MISSIVE

O wifie dear I ask no better
Than getting from yourself a letter;
It comforts me to know you're well
While I'm in thick of shot and shell.
I'm writing this upon my knee
Hiding behind a wee *bit* tree:
Though every moment seems my last,
For seven and forty hours past.

So far I have escaped unhurt
Tho' balls have riddled my old shirt;
My trousers too were cut to shreds
That covered two poor fleshless legs.
Then, as if Heaven sent me help,
I got this parcel from yourself,
With shirts and pants and muffler too,
O wifie dear how kind of you.

Talk of big-wigs and such bluff
Of lords and ladies and such stuff;
But not a man in all my squad
Is half so proud as your old lad
At getting from your own dear hand,
And sent to me from Ireland,
This timely bundle of reminders
From my wee houseful of behinders.

Yes, yes, dear wifie here's a pipe
Tell Davie daddy's goin' to light;
And here's a cut of grand tobacco
For which I thank our dear wee Etta,
And soda farls and cakes galore,
A fowl well savoured, aye, and more,
A wee bit bottle – just a drappie
I'll say no more – O Lord! How happy!

EASTERTIDE

Dear Lord the day of eggs is here
Which many sinners shall revere;
For Saints they do not care so much
Because they move in constant touch
With Thee for sacrificing all
To save the souls of great and small.
This day is dear to everyone
Alive beneath the moon and sun;
Surmounted have you, Gracious Lord,
The pangs of death on Calvary's board,
Your second visit might I say
Is hailed by all this Easter Day.
The Saints are singing carols There,
And free they seem from every care;
While we on Earth this great day keep
By feasting well on eggs and beef.
Thy precious Blood so free from stain
For purity shall aye remain;
I trust, all sinners, who shall bathe
Their sins within that Righteous Wave
Of purest Blood shed on the Cross,
Will hug the gain and lose the loss.
Love is the rolling stone of all,
And often makes large matters small:
So Love if founded upon Trust
Shall ever live — were — we — in — Dust.

from

IRENE IDDESLEIGH

[Sir John Dunfern, retiring forty-year-old bachelor of Dunfern Mansion, receives an invitation from Lord and Lady Dilworth to a ball at Dilworth Castle near Canterbury. He accepts, knowing that among the 'fully-fledged belles' present will be Irene Iddesleigh, Lord Dilworth's adopted daughter, 'more generally known as "The Southern Beauty"'. Sir John is captivated by Irene and hopes to marry her.]

from
CHAPTER FOUR

The month preceding Irene's wedding was one of merriment at Dilworth Castle, Lord and Lady Dilworth extending the social hand of fashionable folly on four different occasions. They seemed drunk with delight that Irene, whom they looked upon as their own daughter, should carry off the palm of purity, whilst affluence, position, and title were for years waiting with restless pride to triumph at its grasp.

It was at the second of these social gatherings that the first seed of jealousy was sown within the breast of Sir John Dunfern, and which had a tendency to remain until it gradually grew to such a rapid state of maturity as to be rooted, if possible, for ever from its dusty bed of ambush.

Yes, when the merriment was at its height, and the heat too oppressive to allow much comfort to the corpulent, the espoused of Irene dropped unexpectedly out of the midst of the aristocratic throng, and being passionately an ardent admirer of the fairy-like fruits of the efforts of the horti-culturist, directed his footsteps towards the well-filled conservatory at the south wing of the building.

The different-shaded lights which dangled from its roof bestowed a look of Indian exquisiteness on the many quaint and delicate productions of nature that rested daintily in their beds of terra-cotta tint.

But before leaving the room he vaguely scanned the throng to catch a glimpse of Irene, and failed to notice her amongst the many who danced so gaily to the well-timed tunes of the celebrated pianist, Charles Wohden, whose musical touch was always capable of melting the most hardened sinner into moods of mellow softness, or cheering the most downcast and raising their drooping look of sadness to that of high-strung hilarity.

Sir John wandered in and out through the numerous windings of sweetest fragrance, until arriving at the farthest corner, of rather darkened shade, and on a wire couch beheld the object of his pursuit, in closest conversation with her tutor, whose name he had altogether failed to remember, only having had the pleasure of his acquaintance a few hours before.

'Can it be possible?' exclaimed Sir John, in profound astonishment. 'Why, I have been searching for you for some time past, and have accidentally found you at last!' Irene, rising to her feet in a second, was utterly dazed, and had the dim lights shewed her proud face to advantage, the ruddy glow of deepest crimson guilt would have manifested itself to a much greater degree. Making multitudinous apologies etc., she at once joined Sir John, who led her back, in apparent triumph, to share the next waltz.

How the true heart beat with growing passion during the remainder of the merry festivity, and as the final announcement of separation was whispered from ear to ear, the gradual wane of Love's lofty right would fain have dwindled into pompous nothing as the thought kept tickling his warm enthusiasm with the nimble fingers of jealousy. That she whom he had ardently hoped should share his future with sheer and loving caresses of constant companionship and wife-like wisdom should be trapped in probably vowing to another her great devotion for him!

But better allow the sickening thought to die on the eve of insult rather than live in the breast of him who, at no distant date, would hear the merry peals of wedding bells ring with gladness, and naturally rejoice at the object of their origin.

CHAPTER FIVE

Our hopes when elevated to that standard of ambition which demands unison may fall asunder like an ancient ruin. They are no longer fit for construction unless on an approved principle. They smoulder away like the ashes of burnt embers, and are cast outwardly from their confined abode, never more to be found where once they existed only as smouldering serpents of scorned pride.

The little chat that Irene apparently enjoyed in the conservatory would gladly have become an act of forgetfulness on her part had not Sir John reminded her of its existence a few days afterwards. The spark of jealous passion had not fully died out after the incident referred to, and awaiting silently its decease, Sir John almost had grown a mourner to its imagined demise, following its undying remains so far as the village of Opportunity, when it was again to revive and shine as luminously as before.

It happened about three weeks preceding the day set apart for their holy union, on Sir John arriving at the castle, he was informed of Irene's recent exit, and gently turning away, he resolved to have a stroll in the tastefully laid-out gardens with the sole object of meeting her.

Walking leisurely along, and stooping to pick up some fallen fruit, he suddenly heard a faint sound issue from amongst the trees. Remaining breathless for a few seconds, lest he might be deceived by the rippling sounds of the adjacent waves, he again heard the same sweet strain, but of much longer duration than before, and quietly moving towards the spot whence it issued, another sound met his ear in the distance, which seemed to be the hasty tread of someone making good an escape, before he got time to view the object he would eagerly have pursued, but checking his desire somewhat, he allowed the matter to sink into silence. Boldly moving towards the spot whence the sound of music issued, how delightfully surprised was he to find a magnificently-constructed little summer-house, a charming pyramidal Gothic structure, robed internally with mossy mantles of nature, and brightened beyond conception with the instrument of humanity which gave origin to such pathetic and sweetened strains.

Politely offering an apology for intruding on the private little palace of Irene, who failed completely to hide her gross confusion from the keen gaze of her espoused, who never seemed to notice in the least the sudden change that swept so swiftly over her pallid cheeks at his unexpected visit, Sir John sat down.

Irene held in her snowy palms a roll of Italian music, which she earnestly endeavoured to conceal from his penetrating stare, probably on account of the words contained therein, which for ever would be unknown to his varied sphere of knowledge, and which would undoubtedly have betrayed her feelings, never dreaming that they should strike other ears than those for whom they practically were intended.

Perceiving her great excitement at the unexpected appearance of him, who ever afterwards kept his jealous thoughts in silent motion, he absolutely evaded making any enquiry whatever, or slightest allusion to the name and nature of the parchment she so firmly retained. Sir John chatted gaily until he gained good ground for delivering to her the message that instinct had so prompted him to utter.

'Irene, my beloved one,' he began, 'it is now only about a score of days until I hoped for ever to call you mine; a hope which unmercifully has haunted me since I fortunately gazed on your lovely face; a hope which I trusted should be fully appreciated by both you and me, and which, I now must own, can never be realised until the clearance of the barrier that since our engagement has been but too apparent.

'The sole object of my visit, my dear Irene' – here Sir John clasped her tender hand in his – 'tonight is to elicit from you a matter that lately has cast a shadowy gloom over my anticipated bright and cheerful future. I am not one of those mortals who takes offence at trifles, neither am I a man of hasty temper or words – quite the contrary, I assure you; but it has, fortunately or unfortunately, been probably a failing amongst my ancestors to court sensitiveness in its minutest detail, and, I must acknowledge, I stray not from any of them in this particular point.

'I must acquaint you, though it pains me deeply to do so, that lately you have not treated me with such respect or attention as you certainly lavished upon me before the announcement of our engagement, and for what reason or reasons I now wish to be apprised. You seem when in company with others to ignore my remarks to you entirely, and treat them with proud disdain, as if shame took the

37

place of pride at my wordy approach! I felt and do feel quite hurt, and am resolved that no such repetition shall take place in future. I promised to be at the castle last night, but unfortunately I felt indisposed, and only that I wished to have a thorough understanding relative to your recent conduct, and which has pained me acutely, I should not have ventured out of doors this evening either. I was, in consequence, obliged to write you last night, asking a written reply, which you failed to give! And this evening, instead of being doubly rejoiced at my presence, you, on the contrary, seem doubly annoyed! I therefore pray, my dearest Irene, that you will, and I am persuaded honestly, not hesitate to satisfy me regarding this unpleasantness, that should anything of which you are now aware cause your conduct to be changed towards me, do not allow it a lair within your breast, but confide in me as thou wouldst in a dearly-trusted and faithful lover.'

At this stage Irene began to consider seriously the earnestness that accompanied the words of Sir John, knowing well she had been guilty, grossly guilty, of the charges with which he impeached her, and which were mixed with child-like simplicity, descriptive only of a world-famed bachelor. She pondered whether or not honesty should take the place of deceit — too often practised in women — and concluded to adopt the latter weapon of defence. Raising her hazel eyes to his, and clearing the weft of truth that had been mixing with the warp of falsehood to form an answer of plausible texture, fringed with different shades of love, she thus began:

'My dearest and much beloved, I assure you your remarks have astounded me not a little! Your words sting like a wasp, though, I am quite convinced, unintentionally. You are well aware that within a short period I will be marked out publicly as mistress of Dunfern mansion — an honour revered in every respect by me; an honour to which I at one time dare never aspire; an honour coveted by many much more worthy than I, whose parentage is as yet bathed in the ocean of oblivious ostentation, until some future day, when I trust it shall stand out boldly upon the brink of disclosure to dry its saturated form and watery wear with the heat of equality. You are about to place me in a position which cannot fail to wring from jealousy and covetousness their flaming torch of abuse. Yes, Sir John, on me you have not ceased to lavish every available treasure and token of your unbounded love. You have been to me not only a loyal admirer, but a thoroughly upright and estimable example of life's purest treasures. You have resolved to place me by your side as your equal, whilst wealth in boundless store is thirsting for your touch. You have elevated my unknown position to such a pitch as to defy taunt or jeer, and at any time if I may have, seemingly, ignored your advances, it was purely want of thought, and not through any underhand motive or scheme whatever.

'I assure you your allusion to my verbal answer last night is very pronounced, and may be overlooked on the ground of pure disappointment. Our time of singleness is now short, and begging your forgiveness for my seeming neglect or indifference, I hope the tide, which until now has flown so gently, may not be stayed on the eve of entering the harbour of harmony, peace, and love.'

At the commencement of Irene's answer of lavishing praises and flimsy apologies, her affianced moved to the opposite corner of the rustic building to scan the features of her he wholly worshipped and relucantly doubted. Every sentence the able and beautiful girl uttered caused Sir John to shift his apparently uncomfortable person nearer and nearer, watching at the same time minutely the divine picture of innocence, until at last, when her reply was ended, he found himself, altogether unconsciously, clasping her to his bosom, whilst the ruby rims which so recently proclaimed accusations and innocence met with unearthly sweetness, chasing every fault over the hills of doubt, until hidden in the hollow of immediate hate.

[When Sir John and Irene return from their honeymoon friction develops because Sir John prefers to stay at home, while his wife yearns for the social prominence once enjoyed by Lord and Lady Dilworth.]

from
CHAPTER EIGHT

Day after day Lady Dunfern pined like a prisoner in her boudoir, and scarcely ever shared a word with the great and good Sir John, who many times wished in former days that she had occupied his home and all its joys. She formed an inward resolution that if prohibited from enjoying life, to which she was accustomed at Dilworth Castle, she would make her husband, whom she knew too well made her his idol, feel the smart, by keeping herself aloof from his caresses as much as possible.

Often would he be found half asleep in deep thought, not having any friend of immediate intimacy in whom he could confide or trust, or to whom he could unbosom the conduct of his wife, whose actions now he was beginning to detest.

The thoughts of disappointment and shame were building for themselves a home of shelter within him – disappointment on account of cherished hopes which unmistakably were crushed to atoms beneath the feet of her who was the sole instigation of their origin; shame, in all probability, lest the love he sought and bought with the price of self might not be his after all! and may still be reserved against his right and kept for another much less worthy! The little jealous spark again revived and prompted him to renew its lustre, which had been hidden for a length of time behind the cloud of dread so silently awaiting the liberty of covering the hill of happiness.

Quietly ruminating over his wife's manner before marriage, about which he was compelled, through observation, to demand an explanation, and pondering carefully her strange and silent habits since it, he became resolved to probe the wound that had swollen so enormously as to demand immediate relief. Ringing furiously for a maid, he handed her a note, to be delivered without delay to Lady Dunfern, the nature of which might well be suspected. Be that as it may, its contents were instrumental in demanding immediate attention.

Soon after its delivery a slight tap was heard at the door of Sir John's study, this room being always his favourite haunt, where he sat beside a bright and glowing fire, engaged in sullen thought; and with an imperious 'Come in!' he still remained in the same thinking posture; nor was he aware, for fully five minutes or so, that his intruder was no other than she whom he so recently ordered into his presence!

Gazing up in a manner which startled the cold-hearted woman not a little, he requested her 'to have a seat right opposite his', to which she instantly complied. At this moment the snow was wafting its flaky handfuls thickly against the barred enclosures of Dunfern Mansion, and chilly as nature appeared outside, it was similarly so indoors for the fond and far-famed husband of Lord Dilworth's charge.

Matters had appeared so unpleasant and altogether bewildering of late that Sir John formed a resolution to bring them to a crisis. Looking fully into the face that seemed so lovely just now, with the dainty spots of blazing ire enlivening the pale cheeks of creeping sin, Sir John began –

'Irene, if I may use such familiarity, I have summoned you hither, it may be to undergo a stricter examination than your present condition probably permits; but knowing, as you should, my life must be miserable under this growing cloud of unfathomed dislike, I became resolved to end, if within my power, such contentious and unladylike conduct as that practised by you towards me of late. It is now quite six months – yea, weary months – since I shielded you from open penury and insult, which were bound to follow you, as well as your much-loved protectors, who sheltered you from the pangs of penniless orphanage; and during these six months, which naturally should have been the pet period of nuptial harmony, it has proved the hideous period of howling dislike!

'I, as you see, am tinged with slightly snowy tufts, the result of stifled sorrow and care concerning you alone; and on the memorable day of our alliance, as you are well aware, the black and glossy locks of glistening glory crowned my brow. There dwelt then, just six months this day, no trace of sorrow or smothered woe – no variety of colour where it is and shall be so long as I exist – no furrows of grief could then be traced upon my visage. But alas, now I feel so changed! And why?

'Because I have dastardly and doggedly been made a tool of treason in the hands of the traitoress and unworthy! I was enticed to believe that an angel was always hovering around my footsteps, when moodily engaged in resolving to acquaint you of my great love, and undying desire to place you upon the highest pinnacle possible of praise and purity within my power to bestow!

'I was led to believe that your unbounded joy and happiness were never at such a par as when sharing them with me.

42

Was I falsely informed of your ways and worth? Was I duped to ascend the ladder of liberty, the hill of harmony, the tree of triumph, and the rock of regard, and when wildly manifesting my act of ascension, was I to be informed of treading still in the valley of defeat?

'Am I, who for nearly forty years was idolised by a mother of untainted and great Christian bearing, to be treated now like a slave? Why and for what am I thus dealt with?

'Am I to foster the opinion that you treat me thus on account of not sharing so fully in your confidence as it may be, another?

'Or is it, can it be, imaginative that you have reluctantly shared, only shared, with me that which I have bought and paid for fully?

'Can it be that your attention has ever been, or is still, attracted by another, who, by some artifice or other, had the audacity to steal your desire for me and hide it beneath his pillaged pillow of poverty, there to conceal it until demanded with my ransom?

'Speak! Irene! Wife! Woman! Do not sit in silence and allow the blood that now boils in my veins to ooze through cavities of unrestrained passion and trickle down to drench me with its crimson hue!

'Speak, I implore you, for my sake, and act no more the deceitful Duchess of Nanté, who, when taken to task by the great Napoleon for refusing to dance with him at a State ball, replied, "You honoured me too highly" – acting the hypocrite to his very face. Are you doing likewise?' Here Sir John, whose flushed face, swollen temples, and fiery looks were the image of indignation, restlessly awaited her reply.

Lady Dunfern began now to stare her position fully in the face. On this interview, she thought, largely depended her future welfare, if viewed properly. Should she make her husband cognisant of her inward feelings, matters were sure

43

to end very unsatisfactorily. These she kept barred against his entrance in the past, and she was fully determined should remain so now, until forced from their home of refuge by spirited action.

Let it be thoroughly understood that Lady Dunfern was forced into a union she never honestly countenanced. She was almost compelled, through the glittering polish Lady Dilworth put on matters, to silently resign the hand of one whose adoration was amply returned, and enter into a contract which she could never properly complete. All she could now do was to plunge herself into the lake of evasion and answer him as best she could.

'Sir and husband,' she said, with great nervousness at first, 'you have summoned me hither to lash your rebuke unmercifully upon me, provoked, it may be, by underhand intercourse. You accordingly, in the course of your remarks, fail not to tamper with a character which as yet defies your scathing criticism. Only this week have I been made the recipient of news concerning my deceased parents, of whom I never before obtained the slightest clue, and armed with equality, I am in a position fit to treat some of your stingy remarks with the scorn they merit.

'You may not already be aware of the fact that I, whom you insinuate you wrested from beggary, am the only child of the late Colonel Iddesleigh, who fell a victim to a gunshot wound inflicted by the hand of his wife, who had fallen into the pit of intemperance. Yes, Earl Peden's daughter was his wife and my mother, and only that this vice so actuated her movements, I might still have lent to Society the object it dare not now claim, and thereby would have shunned the iron rule of being bound down to exist for months at a time within such a small space of the world's great bed.

'If my manner has changed in any way since our union, of it I am not aware, and fail to be persuaded of any existing difference, only what might be attributed to Lady Dilworth's sudden and unexpected removal from our midst, which occasioned me grief indeed.

'It behoves elderly men like you to rule their wives with jealous supervision, especially if the latter tread on the fields of youth. Such is often fictitious and unfounded altogether, and should be treated with marked silence.

'I may here say I was mistress, in a measure, of my movements whilst under the meek rule of Lady Dilworth; nor was I ever thwarted in any way from acting throughout her entire household as I best thought fit, and since I have taken upon me to hold the reins of similarity within these walls, I find they are much more difficult to manage. I, more than once, have given orders which were completely prohibited from being executed. By whom, might I ask, and why? Taking everything into consideration, I am quite justified in acquainting you that, instead of being the oppressor, I feel I am the oppressed.

'Relative to my affections, pray have those courted by me in the past aught to do with the present existing state of affairs? I am fully persuaded to answer, "Nothing whatever."

'You speak of your snowy tufts appearing where once there dwelt locks of glossy jet. Well, I am convinced they never originated through me, and must surely have been threatening to appear before taking the step which links me with their origin.

'I now wish to retire, feeling greatly fatigued, and trusting our relations shall remain friendly and mutual, I bid thee good-night.'

Lady Dunfern swept out of the room, and hurrying to her own apartment, burst into an uncontrollable fit of grief.

[Lady Dunfern gives birth to a son. In delirium she declares her love for her tutor, Oscar Otwell, and is imprisoned by Sir John but escapes with Otwell. Financial difficulties drive the latter to intemperance, violence to Irene and finally suicide. Sir John, seriously ill, recovers sufficiently before his death to reveal to young Hugh Dunfern the truth about Irene.]

CHAPTER EIGHTEEN

Mocking Angel! The trials of a tortured throng are naught when weighed in the balance of future anticipations. The living sometimes learn the touchy tricks of the traitor, the tardy, and the tempted; the dead have evaded the flighty earthly future, and form to swell the retinue of retired rights, the righteous school of the invisible, and the rebellious roar of raging nothing.

The night was dark and tempestuous; the hill rather inclined to be steep; the clouds were bathed in wrinkled furrows of vapoury smoke; the traffic on the quiet and lonely roads surrounding Dunfern Mansion was utterly stopped, and nature seemed a block of obstruction to the eye of the foreigner who drudged so wearily up the slope that led to the home of Mrs Durand, who had been confined to bed for the past three years, a sufferer from rheumatism.

Perceiving the faint flicker of light that occasionally flung its feeble rays against the dim fanlight of faithful Fanny's home – the aged sister of the late Tom Hepworth – the two-fold widowed wanderer, with trembling step, faltered to the door of uncertain refuge, and, tapping against it with fingers cold and stiff, on such a night of howling wind and beating rain, asked, in weakened accents, the woman who opened to her the door, 'if she could be allowed to remain for the night?' – a request that was granted through charity alone. After relieving herself of some outer garments, and partaking of the slight homely fare kindly ordered by Mrs Durand, the widow of Oscar Otwell and Sir John Dunfern warmed herself and dried her saturated clothing before going to bed. She had just arrived the day previous, and hastened to take up her abode as near her former home of exquisiteness as she could, without detection.

On extinguishing the light before retiring, and casting one glance in the direction of the little window, the innumerable recollections of the abundant past swept across the mind of the snowy-haired widow, and were further augmented by the different star-like lights which shone from the numerous windows in Dunfern Mansion, directly opposite where she lay.

A couple of days found her almost rested after such a trying night as that on which she arrived, and observing the sharpest reticence lest she might be known, she nerved herself to appear next day at Dunfern Mansion, to accomplish the last wish of her late lover and husband, for whom she ventured so much and gained so little, and particularly to try and see her son.

The morning was warm and fine; numerous birds kept chirping outside the little cottage of Mrs Durand. The widow, with swollen eyes and face of faded fear, prepared herself for the trying moment, which she was certain of achieving. Partaking of a very slight breakfast, she told Mrs Durand not to expect her for dinner.

Marching down the hill's face, she soon set foot on the main road that led directly to Dunfern Mansion. Being admitted by Nancy Bennet, a prim old dame, who had been in charge of the lodge for the last eighteen years, the forlorn widow, whose heart sank in despair as she slowly walked up the great and winding avenue she once claimed, reached the huge door through which she had been unconsciously carried by Marjory Mason a good many years ago.

Gently ringing the bell, the door was attended by a strange face. Reverently asking to have an interview with Sir John Dunfern, how the death-like glare fell over the eyes of the disappointed as the footman informed her of his demise! 'Madam, if you cast your eyes thence' – here the sturdy footman pointed to the family graveyard, lying quite adjacent, and in which the offcast of effrontery had oftentimes trodden – ' you can with ease behold the rising symbol of death which the young nobleman, Sir Hugh Dunfern, has lavishly and unscrupulously erected to his fond memory.'

The crushed hopes of an interview with the man she brought with head of bowed and battered bruises, of blasted untruths and astounding actions, to a grave of premature solitude were further crumbled to atoms in an instant. They were driven beyond retention, never again to be fostered with feverish fancy. After the deplorable news of her rightful husband's death had been conveyed to the sly and shameless questioner, who tried hard to balance her faintish frame unobserved, she asked an interview with Sir Hugh Dunfern. This also was denied, on the ground of absence from home.

Heavily laden with the garb of disappointment did the wandering woman of wayward wrong retrace her footsteps from the door for ever, and leisurely walked down the artistic avenue of carpeted care, never more to face the furrowed frowns of friends who, in years gone by, bestowed on her the praises of poetic powers. Forgetful almost of her present movements, the dangerous signal of widowhood was seen to float along the family graveyard of the Dunferns.

Being beforehand acquaint with the numerous and costly tombstones erected individually, regardless of price, the wearied and sickly woman of former healthy tread was not long in observing the latest tablet, of towering height, at the north-east end of the sacred plot.

There seemed a touchy stream of gilded letters carefully cut on its marble face, and on reading them with watery eye and stooping form, was it anything remarkable that a flood of tears bathed the verdure that peeped above the soil?

The lines were these:

I

The hand of death hath once more brought
   The lifeless body here to lie,
Until aroused with angels' voice,
   Which call it forth, no more to die.

II

This man, of health and honest mind,
   Had troubles great to bear whilst here,
Which cut him off, in manhood's bloom,
   To where there's neither frown nor tear.

III

His life was lined with works of good
   For all who sought his affluent aid;
His life-long acts of charity
   Are sure to never pass unpaid.

IV

Sir John Dunfern, whose noble name
   Is heard to echo, far and wide;
In homes of honour, truth, and right,
   With which he here lies side by side.

V

The wings of love and lasting strength
   Shall flap above his hollow bed;
Angelic sounds of sweetest strain
   Have chased away all tears he shed.

Then, when the glorious morn shall wake
  Each member in this dust of ours,
To give to each the sentence sure
  Of everlasting Princely Power –

He shall not fail to gain a seat
  Upon the bench of gloried right,
To don the crown of golden worth
  Secured whilst braving Nature's fight.

After carefully reading these lines the figure of melting woe sat for a long time in silence until a footstep came up from behind, which alarmed her not a little. Looking up she beheld the face of a youth whose expression was very mournful, and asking after her mission, was informed she had been casting one last look on the monument of her lamented husband.

'Mighty Heavens!' exclaimed Sir Hugh Dunfern, 'are you the vagrant who ruined the very existence of him whom you now profess to have loved? You, the wretch of wicked and wilful treachery, and formerly the wife of him before whose very bones you falsely kneel! Are you the confirmed traitoress of the trust reposed in you by my late lamented, dearest, and most noble of fathers? Are you aware that the hypocrisy you manifested once has been handed down to me as an heirloom of polluted possession, and stored within this breast of mine, an indelible stain for life, or, I might say, during your known and hated existence?

'False woman! Wicked wife! Detested mother! Bereft widow!

'How darest thou set foot on the premises your chastity should have protected and secured! What wind of transparent touch must have blown its blasts of boldest bravery around your poisoned person and guided you within miles of the mansion I proudly own?

'What spirit but that of evil used its influence upon you to dare to bend your footsteps of foreign tread towards the door through which they once stole unknown? Ah, woman of sin and stray companion of tutorism, arise, I demand you, and strike across that grassy centre as quickly as you can, and never more make your hated face appear within these mighty walls. I can never own you; I can never call you mother; I cannot extend the assistance your poor, poverty-stricken attire of false don silently requests; neither can I ever meet you on this side the grave, before which you so pityingly kneel!'

Speechless and dogged did the dishonoured mother steal for ever from the presence of her son, but not before bestowing one final look at the brightened eye and angry countenance of him who loaded on her his lordly abuse. The bowed form of former stateliness left for ever the grounds she might have owned without even daring to offer one word of repentance or explanation to her son.

Walking leisurely along the road that reached Dilworth Castle, how the trying moments told upon her who shared in pangs of insult and poverty! — how the thoughts of pleasant days piled themselves with parched power upon the hilltop of remembrance and died away in the distance! The whirling brain became more staid as she heard the approach of horses' feet, and stopping to act the part of Lot's wife, gave such a haggard stare at the driver of the vehicle as caused him to make a sudden halt. Asking her to have a seat, the weary woman gladly mounted upon its cushion with thankfulness, and alighted on reaching its journey's end, about three miles from Audley Hall. The drive was a long one, and helped to rest the tired body of temptation.

Returning thanks to the obliging driver, she marched wearily along until she reached the home of her first refuge after flight.

Perceiving the yellow shutters firmly bolted against the light admitters of Audley Hall, she feared disappointment was also waiting her. Knocking loudly twice before any attempt was made to open the door, there came at last an aged man with halting step and shaking limb.

'Is Major Iddesleigh at home?' asked the saddened widow.

'Oh, madam, he has been dead almost twelve years, and since then no one has occupied this Hall save myself, who am caretaker. The Marquis of Orland was deceived by his nephew, who sold it in an underhand manner to the major, and he resolved that never again would he allow it to be occupied since the major's death by any outsider.'

'You are rather lonely,' said the widow.

'Yes, yes,' replied he, 'but I have always been accustomed living alone, being an old bachelor, and wish to remain so. It is better to live a life of singleness than torture both body and soul by marrying a woman who doesn't love you, like the good Sir John Dunfern – a nobleman who lived only some miles from this, and who died lately broken-hearted – who became so infatuated with an upstart of unknown parentage, who lived in Dilworth Castle, with one Lord Dilworth, the previous owner, that he married her offhand, and, what was the result, my good woman? – why she eventually ran off with a poor tutor! and brought the hairs of hoary whiteness of Sir John Dunfern to the grave much sooner than in all probability they would have, had he remained like me.'

Facing fumes of insult again, thought the listener. And asking after Major Iddesleigh's will, eagerly awaited his reply.

Placing one hand upon her shoulder, and pointing with

the other, 'Behold,' said he, 'yonder church? that was his last will – Iddesleigh Church. It was only when the jaws of death gaped for their prey that the major was forced to alter his will, having had it previously prepared in favour of his niece, whose whereabouts could never be traced until after his death.'

'Enough – enough, I must go,' said the painful listener, and thanking the old man for his information, which, like her son's, had screwed its bolts of deadly weight more deeply down on the lid of abstract need, turned her back on Audley Hall for ever.

CHAPTER NINETEEN

Hope sinks a world of imagination. It in almost every instance never fails to arm the opponents of justice with weapons of friendly defence, and gains their final fight with peaceful submission. Life is too often stripped of its pleasantness by the steps of false assumption, marring the true path of life-long happiness which should be pebbled with principle, piety, purity, and peace.

Next morning, after the trying adventure of the lonely outcast, was the scene of wonder at Dilworth Castle. Henry Hawkes, the head gardener under the Marquis of Orland, on approaching the little summer-house in which Irene Iddesleigh so often sat in days of youth, was horrified to find the dead body of a woman, apparently a widow, lying prostrate inside its mossy walls. 'Lord, protect me!' shouted poor Hawkes, half distractedly, and hurried to Dilworth Castle to inform the inmates of what he had just seen.

They all rushed towards the little rustic building to verify the certainty of the gardener's remarks. There she lay, cold, stiff, and lifeless as Nero, and must have been dead for hours. They advised the authorities, who were soon on the spot.

What stinging looks of shame the Marquis cast upon her corpse on being told that it was that of the once beautiful Lady Dunfern — mother of the present heir to Dunfern estate.

Lying close at hand was an old and soiled card, with the words almost beyond distinction, 'Irene Iddesleigh'. In an instant her whole history flashed before the unforgiving mind of the Marquis, and being a sharer in her devices, through his nephew Oscar Otwell, ordered her body to be conveyed to the morgue, at the same time intimating to Sir Hugh Dunfern her demise.

It transpired at the inquest, held next day, that she was admitted the previous night to the grounds of Dilworth Castle by the porter at the lodge, giving her name as 'Irene Iddesleigh'.

She must have taken refuge in the little construction planned under her personal supervision whilst inhabiting Dilworth Castle during her girlhood, and, haunted with the never-dying desire to visit once more its lovely grounds, wandered there to die of starvation.

No notice whatever was taken of her death by her son, who obeyed to the last letter his father's instructions, and carried them out with tearless pride.

The little narrow bed at the lowest corner on the west side of Seaforde graveyard was the spot chosen for her remains. Thus were laid to rest the orphan of Colonel Iddesleigh, the adopted daughter and imagined heiress of Lord and Lady Dilworth, what might have been the proud wife of Sir John Dunfern, the unlawful wife of Oscar Otwell, the suicidal outcast, and the despised and rejected mother.

She who might have swayed society's circle with the sceptre of nobleness – she who might still have shared in the greatness of her position and defied the crooked stream of poverty in which she so long sailed – had she only been, first of all, true to self, then the honourable name of Sir John Dunfern would have maintained its standard of pure and noble distinction, without being spotted here and there with heathenish remarks inflicted by a sarcastic public on the administerer of proper punishment; then the dignified knight of proud and upright ancestry would have been spared the pains of incessant insult, the mockery of equals, the haunted diseases of mental trials, the erring eye of harshness, and the throbbing twitch of constant criticism.

It was only the lapse of a few minutes after the widowed waif left Dunfern Mansion until the arrival of her son from London, who, after bidding his mother quit the grounds owned by him, blotted her name for ever from his book of memory; and being strongly prejudiced by a father of faultless bearing, resolved that the sharers of beauty, youth, and false love should never have the slighest catch on his affections.

from

FUMES OF FORMATION

THE END OF 'PAIN'

Great Mercy! May I now give vent
To that which brings me sweet content!
The passing of a 'Pain' who tore
The efforts of the gifted more
Than others of a 'wormy' breed
Extracted from diluted seed.

That 'Pain' has ceased to mock, to mar
Those gems he picked up near and far,
Is evident. His pricky pen
Reclaim it ne'er shall he again.
A mighty maggot, He thought he,
A slavey now to Master D.

He, in his glassless backroom bare,
Can flaunt his sheets of 'blarney' there,
No more shall his erratic brain
E'er blank the works of men of fame,
Or women on whom men rely
To stock the Earth with human 'fry'.

Great Mercy! I shall say no more
But ask and answer as of yore:
Why should all such 'rodents of State'
Have scope to nibble – genius great?
The answer is – they're bare of bread,
Their only food – a brilliant head.

[Written in 1928 to mark the death
of the critic Barry Pain]

EXTEMPORE

On being asked by a digit of dollardom, USA,
to write a few lines on front page of
Irene Iddesleigh, *I gave him the following:*

What a fool art thou my dear man
   To ask for a daub of my pen,
With which to enrich your ambition
   And place you above other men.
Assuming you're wise I now send you
   A stroke of my purest and best:
So here's to your health when I'm dreaming
   Of you and your foolish request.

*On being asked by a dispenser of spiritual foppery, whom
I lately met at the house of a friend, to pour from one of
my tiny brain-cells a little drop of poetry, instantly and
original, allowing me five minutes for composition, I gave
him the following in thirty seconds:*

Thank God for this your proud Apostle,
Though into this world he came
As bare as Lazarus, now to jostle
With a beggar he'd think shame.

from

DELINA DELANEY

[Joe Delaney, a Connemara fisherman, dies of exposure after helping to rescue some shipwrecked sailors, and his wife and only child, Delina, are left destitute. Lady Gifford employs Delina as a seamstress who quickly arouses the interest of the young Lord Gifford. Lady Gifford determines to prevent the development of the relationship, but Lord Gifford persists and the couple are betrothed. Their conversation is overheard by the jealous Lady Mattie Maynard, who relates it to her aunt, Lady Gifford, on her return from London.]

from
CHAPTER SIX

It was Lady Gifford's custom for the past two years to leave her niece in full charge at the Castle in her absence, and the belief appearing before her repeatedly, fabricated by self-desire, led her to imagine she so mothered the law that at this very stage when she was revelling in confidence that she possessed the reins of mingled kindred, they were torn from her powerless grasp with beggared pride.

Lord Gifford sat burying in the silver receptacle that lay by his side the deadened ashes of feathery manufacture produced by the action of his thin lips. The sweet memory of past utterances trembled through him like an electric shock, and sent a diametrical streak of deep red, round which rested a paler-coloured circumference of natural shade, proving pleasingly effectual on his ghostly cheek, that served as a striking background. 'Conqueror', the name of a favourite little dog that accompanied Lady Gifford when at home, in all her outdoor visits, commenced just now to bark rapturously, as he stood at Lord Gifford's feet, on hearing the sound of wheels, and in a few minutes more Lady Gifford entered. Walking smartly past her son's door, she was escorted to her room by Lady Mattie. This was not customary, for Lady Gifford always before entered the room of her son first on her arrival. Sorrow fell upon Lord Gifford as he heard his mother's voice above. Piqued somewhat, he grinned sneeringly at Conqueror, who abated not his joyous bark until Lord Gifford opened the door and allowed him into the hall.

Lady Mattie had lost tremendously in spirit and look, her aunt thought; and, fired with a blazing desire to find out the cause, said, in raised tones: 'But, "Mat"' – this was her favourite name for Lady Mattie – 'you look dreadful. Why, it seems as if death had visited the Castle since I left. I hope everything has gone on well with you, and that my chief wish is at least bordering on fulfilment?'

Continuing, Lady Gifford said, 'What a funny thing it seems to me that you appear so disheartened and dispirited, somehow, leaving you, as I did, so bright and gay a few months ago. What, I say, is it all about?' spake Lady Gifford, emphatically, taking a seat close beside her niece.

Lady Mattie, whose faced looked rather dangerous just now, wept copiously, refusing for a time to be consoled, even by her kind benefactress.

Lady Gifford jumped to her feet, vociferating loudly that she must call in her son for an explanation. This stayed the melting action of Lady Mattie, who, in ragged accents, begged her aunt to sit down.

'Then tell me at once,' demanded her ladyship, with a slight stamp of her foot, that convinced Lady Mattie she was in solemn earnest.

Lady Mattie then unbosomed the conversation that took place between Lord Gifford and the 'little fisherwoman', as she angrily termed her unreasonable rival.

The twisting of the proud face, the wringing of the gloved hands (for Lady Gifford hadn't relieved herself of a single article since her entrance), the excitable movements of her well-clad body, all bespake the blow of disgrace and indignation from which she painfully suffered. Powers now came to the surface that hitherto had been buried deep, deep in the grace of nidulant dormancy. Raising her flashing eyes towards heaven, she groaned aloud:

'Ah, heavenly Father!'

Another silent moment, and she turned to Lady Mattie with the words:

'But how came you, under heaven, to know all this? God forbid that there is a scrap of truth in what you say!' said the distracted mother.

Wiping her eyes, and clearing her throat completely of any little mucus that perchance would serve to obstruct the tone of her resolute explanation, she said, in a decisive mood:

'My dear aunt, I am only too well convinced of the truth of what I've told you to doubt its genuineness. As I have already informed you, when I saw your son, my cousin, lead that low-bred, vulgar atom towards the garden, I went to the tent in order, if possible, to find out the object of the visit. The large rustic couch rests right behind it; this I know, and fancying they might recline on its wooden breast, I concluded I might overhear for what purpose he had brought her. I overheard every word distinctly, and no mouth save his own could or would have uttered such language about me. Such disparaging, ungentlemanly discourse I never heard; and, what makes the matter ten times more terrible, his profession of reverence for me while in my company was all that could possibly belong to your son. I all but fainted at his dreadful remarks, and throwing down the pamphlet I held, ran here as fast as my strength enabled me – God alone knows how I ever got the length, I felt so. I remained here for some time, pacing my floor restlessly, when I was prompted again to visit the tent. Their voices still I heard professing attachment to each other; and more I've yet to tell, my loving aunt, which I before refrained to do: he gave her a ring, and – and – and –' (Lady Mattie's voice now became tremulous) '– asked her to be his – wife!'

Tightly clasping her hands, now stripped of their covering, Lady Gifford shrieked, 'Good God!' The first act of gallantry observed by her bestowed upon the seamstress by her son mounted into her burning eyeballs with shooting scorn, as she brought it before her with prominence, and other marks of disliking fidelity during Delina's post of seamstress at the Castle could not fail either to stand in her view, like so many fiends. Casting on the floor, with an angry waft of her jewelled hand, the many valuable purchases made in London, that nestled closely on the table by her side, she fled wildly to her son's apartment, followed by Lady Mattie.

She found him lying cushioned in a corner of the room, evidently enjoying interesting anecdotes from the pen of the witty mass of immobility that graced the opposite corner of his dazzling haunt. The glaring contrast between the lifeless statue of the renowned Scottish wag, who cast such chagrin upon the noisy intruder with eyes of calmest blindness, and that of his ardent admirer's approacher, would have given to the hand of a Rubens a final mark of unsurpassed and everlasting fame.

Right well Lord Gifford knew, as he heard her pace the floor overhead, that Lady Mattie had been lavishing torrents of abuse about him, the true nature of which, he felt assured, he was partly ignorant. He had not the remotest guess that the bomb of strife, so artfully prepared by the tongue of levelled indignation, would thus explode by the force of high-bred egotism.

'Home again, Mother?' he boldly uttered, as he gazed reverently in her face.

'Home to Hades!' returned the raging, high-bred daughter of distinguished effeminacy.

'Ah me! what is the matter?' meekly enquired his lordship.

'Everything is the matter with a broken-hearted mother of low-minded offspring,' she answered, hotly.

'The cup of wrath has been offered you at boiling point, and you had not the spirited courage to resist it, I'm afraid,' rejoined her son.

Rising to her feet, and tossing her haughty head as high as she reasonably could without pain, she commenced to pace the floor in deepest agony.

Whilst these moments of heated passion were moving into the abyss of abject wonder, Lady Mattie Maynard sat criticising silently the cool composure of her cousin, never speaking yet a word in his presence that might add to her aunt's vocabulary of vindictive dissyllables about to be expressed.

Lady Gifford, whose tall, stern form bore itself mightily for some moments, with an almost overpowering air curtailing the resolute look of her son to a lowering glance, at last broke forth, in a borrowed voice ending in a painfully high-strung pitch:

'Henry Edward Ludlow Gifford, son of my strength, idolised remnant of my inert husband, who at this moment invisibly offers the scourging whip of fatherly authority to your backbone of resentment (though for years you think him dead to your movements) and pillar of maternal trust.'

Then, raising her huge dark eyes towards heaven until

hidden underneath their appointed protection, she prayed, in accents that threaten to vibrate against the starry ceiling until this day:

'Heavenly Pater,' she began, 'listen to the words of a daughter of affliction, and chase, I pray Thee, instantly, the dismal perplexities that presently clog the filmy pores of her weary brain into the stream of trickling nothingness. Bind their origin with cloth of coloured shame, and restore, Thou, her equilibrium with draughts of soothing good.'

Exhausted with rage, the voice grew weak, the limbs unsteady, the face pallid with anger.

Lord Gifford stood mightily moved, and conducted her to a chair.

'Oh, Mother, are you mad?' he muttered, pale as death.

'Mad?' she said, 'Your mother, Lady Gifford, mad? No, good sir; God forbid!'

Continuing, she said: 'I know I am a weak, sinful mortal. Thou knowest this, my Father, and charged with a duty I feel I must perform to the best of my ability, but not without Thine holy aid and guidance. Kindly stay the progress of everlasting shame that is about to stain the proud ancestral home of peace that shelters me in its rooms of comfort; tear asunder the tie of friendship that at this time threatens to become stronger; burn it to atoms in an unseen sightless blaze. Remove the strength, the will – nay, I would almost say the perpetrator – from the headstrong path of performance on which he treads so resolutely, and fill his vacant pores with the liquid of obedience and self-respect, trampling thereby under his feet all thoughts and actions likely to prove both hideous and grievously vexing!'

Lady Gifford, who again became exhausted, lifted the burning hand of blazing touch and laid it on her moistened brow, already beaded with Nature's dew. Standing erect (for she was one of those fine figures at all times worthy of admiration), she measured her nervous height against the marble support, that unknowingly offered her its giant aid, and, in a voice of deep parental pathos, exclaimed:

'Take me to Thyself, my God! Take me at once, that I shall escape the pain, the daring insult, of seeing the house and honourable old name of Gifford plunge into shame! Death before disgrace — yes, twice welcome! "Death before dishonour" has been our gallant crest of thirty decades, and never, oh! never has it been daubed or speckled for a triple century! But now it is about to be blotted, blighted, and buried, to be known no more as ours. Oh, God, how my brain reels! Have I, at this opportune moment, a perfect grasp of my senses?'

Palpitating silence followed, Lady Gifford strongly impressing upon her son and niece that the earnestness with which she so openly expressed her selfish prayer was real, not imaginary. She, by her words of ringing bitterness, brought the object of her rebuke close beside the poet's companion, not to join in her remarks, but to wield the flail of lashing taunt that laid such heavy strokes upon his mind of misty and complicated conjecture.

'Mother, I again ask, are you mad?' said Lord Gifford, in grave tones. 'What is the cause of all this?' Before he gave her time to answer him a word in reply, he turned towards her abettor, whose writhing countenance convinced him he was not about to address the absentee to guilt. 'Lady Mattie, can you enlighten me anything regarding my mother's idiotic movements? What does or can all this mean?' madly asked he, who, as yet, was totally unaware that any creature save Delina was owner of the words spoken by him in the garden's fragrant silence.

Lady Mattie's time at last had come to address the questioner in tones of sharpened dislike, and, summoning all her angry courage, she thus replied:

'Henry Gifford, owner of a title that has been wrongly reached you by the hand of legal ancestry, I fear not, at this trying moment, to answer your questions of seeming innocence in the same tone as that in which you instructed your idol of piscatory perfection in the branches of my residence at Columba Castle, &c. First, if I thought your mother's movements bordered on insanity, I should answer your pithy question with impartial pride, but perceiving clearly the sensible spirit in which she has uttered her words of surprise at your projected alliance with the beggared offspring of illiteration in its most loathing light, it remains for me to answer that question with words of cursing silence. Your second order of hasty howl I shall be pleased to make more definite. It was Lady Mattie Maynard who not alone supplied the thread, but constructed the ball that your good mother, my kind and devoted aunt, has only lamely struck, and hopes to come off at least victorious through its bouncing worth. Lastly, all I've got to say is, of its meaning you cannot be ignorant.' And Lady Mattie, rising, quitted the room followed by Lady Gifford.

Lord Gifford, shocked somewhat at the electric truth of his cousin's remarks, walked silently into the verandah to breathe an air of momentary freedom, evidently denied him in the presence of his disturbed mother and angry cousin.

When left to themselves to formulate their ideas into strains of determination, the proud, stern mother and perverse niece stood discussing the marked indignation that loomed from the eyes of Lord Gifford, and, after a few strong fancies swept across their disordered brains, they commenced to fear the friction, the combined force of their words, aroused in the breast of Lord Gifford, might not add much, if further augmented, to their happiness that hitherto prevailed throughout Columba Castle, and judiciously agreed to stay any existing evidence of their anger or disapproval until further disclosures would be forthcoming that would practically convince them of the propriety of its bestowal.

[Lord Gifford and Delina flee to Clapham Hall in London, where Gifford employs the sinister Madam-de-Maine as governess–companion to his wife. While Gifford is in Ireland, Madam-de-Maine begins to tyrannise Delina, who takes flight. She is knocked down by a runaway horse and in the hospital where she recovers becomes a trainee nurse. Meanwhile, Lord Gifford, having searched for Delina without success, deteriorates to a point where he is at the mercy of Madam-de-Maine. When he has an accident, she keeps him in a brandy-sodden stupor, drawing upon herself the impassioned denunciations of the faithful servant, Joss Danvers. While she is away in London, a nurse is appointed to look after Lord Gifford. It is Delina!]

CHAPTER NINETEEN

Nurse Delaney saluted him with a graceful bow. He made an effort to raise himself on his elbow, an act he utterly failed to accomplish, and gasped in a low, painful voice:

'Never – never! It cannot be – it cannot be!' at the same time holding out his hot, feverish hands. He could no longer mistake the fact that this was his own darling that was lost and found, about whom he grieved so much, and almost ruined his existence.

Dr Norton, whose chief concentration was upon her, stood puzzled and baffled at their meeting.

Often girls are quick to detect interest in themselves, promoted often by the opposite sex; but Nurse Delaney was too wholly engrossed just now with the dashing force of

Fate to notice a slight quiver on the doctor's lip, or the quick heaving of his breast.

Dr Norton was always reckoned a self-possessed man, somewhat reserved and slightly shy; but the handsome face of Nurse Delaney, outlined in girlish innocence, had so figured its fairness on his heart that he shook under the merest look that would tend to win her affection. He was aware she was only a girl, her pores incapable yet of the tiniest stream of love, he thought, to trickle through them; and with the strong nerve of one labouring beneath a load of hope, he immediately checked the tenderness of his passion, that leaped within him, blinding her against the shock his emotion had sustained, and donned again that nature he knew before he met her. Controlling the tremor of his deep passion, he said to Nurse Delaney, who sat bathed in tears:

'You know your patient, then, Nurse?'

'I – I have met him – before,' she stammered.

'Oh!' returned the doctor, totally puzzled, pulling rather unmercifully the ends of his silver moustache. Having some professional calls to make, he thought the sooner he now performed them the better for all concerned. After carefully instructing her how to treat Lord Gifford, and dwelling emphatically on the words 'On no account allow Madam-de-Maine to offer him anything without my express permission', he left Clapham Hall to listen to the childish complaints of a mother whose boy had got his finger slightly burned; to sympathise with the feverish father, and prescribe for him the usual remedies; to administer a soothing draught to the maid charged with a lingering consumption; and, after performing these duties to his entire satisfaction, to enter his home and brood over the current events of the day. There are stillnesses more awful than words of tender recollection – ghastly images more heartrending than death.

Nurse Delaney sat terror-bound, after the doctor's exit, at the tied-up forehead and lip, the deathly glare of his dark eyes, the awful pallor of the visible portions of his face, the thin, hot hands that still clasped hers with forced grasp, and the shattered, slim frame of the robust lover she not so long ago had known.

He lay back, exhausted with the overpowering stroke of joy, of which he had lost all hopes. All his doubts now had fled as mist before a sunray; his brain rolled; he violently shook. Silence claimed him; sorrow disowned him. At times he lay apparently lifeless and motionless; at others breathing heavily, and tumbling to and fro. The recollection of her departure cast him senseless; the exultant leap of her recovery blurred his understanding.

She threw her tender arms around him, weeping copiously; she kissed his cheek and hands, stroked the bandage on his painful brow, whispering words of courage to soothe him in an hour of which Nature seemed to rob him; she fondled and caressed him as if a helpless infant; every spark of sympathetic tenderness was alive in her at the grasp of his suffering.

He opened his eyes of deadly flare, and closed them, not conscious who stood watching over him.

'Ah, my own Lord Gifford,' she said, leaning over the emaciated body, 'don't you know me? Don't you know Delina Delaney, you used to love?' She flung herself across the bed, hiding herself from another terrible and painful stare.

'He will never get better – never!' she groaned, sobbing aloud.

He lay as noticeless of her dreadful agony as he was unconscious of his own.

She rose, bent over him again and again, saying:

'I love you, I love you, dear Lord Gifford! Delina loves you still!'

Not a muscle moved. He lay now still, as if in a slumber.

She resolved not to disturb him for a goodly time, earnestly praying that out of this form of rest he'd awake, conscious that she was with him at last to succour and strengthen him in his hour of distress.

The hollow-hearted are numerous; the genuine-hearted rare. Scarce, whom Nature honestly leadeth; plentiful, who falsifies her endeavours.

Still slumbering, Nurse Delaney let him rest. She thought the pain had ceased, mentally and bodily, and bore up her strength with the hope that quietness would shorten the journey of pain.

Moving to the window, her attention was drawn to the tall figure of a woman making across the road towards the gate that led to Clapham Hall. As she passed lightly along, walking on tip-toe, anxious to gain the door unobserved in a measure, which, so far, she had not done. It was Madam-de-Maine — no mistake whatever about it. Her very shadow ran through Nurse Delaney like a stream of icy water. She dreaded meeting her in her present capacity, and, in fact, at almost any risk. She loathed, with terror dancing on every feature, meeting this woman, through whose rough usage she was obliged to bend the yoke that once bound her in faith to her lover. Many a pang of sorrow rent her young heart since then.

Instantly Madam-de-Maine entered her first enquiries were about the doctor's visit.

'Was he accompanied by anyone?' she smartly demanded.

'By a nurse,' the maid replied.

'Hang the old puppy!' she vociferated, bit her lip with an intensity not usual, and smartly tripping towards the patient's room, she had an encounter with old Joss, whom she chanced to meet in the lobby.

'Now, mae wumman,' said Joss, with a certain amount of bravo in his tone, 'Oi've fixed ye! Gwin dthere,' pointing with his short, rough finger, 'an' ye'll mibbe see what 'ill sittle ye. Ye'll nat git doin' is ye loike now – pity ye shud! Mae good masther's sleepin', dthe noice wee attindint tills me, an' it's maeself dthat's wearyin' ta hiv 'im an his feet agane.'

A smart slap on the ear was the only practical reply Joss received from Madam-de-Maine, as she rushed into the sick-room, not forgetting to turn the key, lest Joss would follow her. A hasty glance at Nurse Delaney woke within her old remembrances. She grew first a mahogany colour, then, as if magically, a ghastly white swept over every feature. Despite all previously-conceived efforts, Nurse Delaney sat as if glued to her chair. Viewing her with eyes of flashing fire, sickening sparks shooting from their intense sheen, she concluded that something more than sympathy for her patient lay closeted in her beating breast.

'Back again to Clapham Hall?' she said, with a sort of cynical sneer.

'Back again,' Nurse Delaney softly replied.

'For what length of time, pray?'

'Lord Gifford will, I presume, decide that matter.'

'You look fancy, to be sure, in nurses' garb! Mockery, by heavens, mockery, and the height of it!' she loudly exclaimed, making for the bedside of the slumbering patient. Peacefully he seemed to rest, to her gross vexation. She rushed to the door, unfastened it, closed it after her, muttering along the corridor:

'Devil take that little fisherwoman! Never mind, I'll make it hot for the urchin – that I will!'

Standing concealed behind a heavy portière, old Joss listened, with every nerve unstrung, for her return. As these last words died on her lips, he popped out triumphantly from his place of ambush.

'An' so ye'll make it hat fur dthe orchin, will ye? 'Dade, in be hivins, Oi'll make it as hat fur yerself, fur Oi'll watch fur dthe dacther ta-marra, an' till 'im ivery wo-ord ye sade; Oi'll put 'im an dthe thrack iv watchin' ye. It's dthe divil's loife ye give till aal iv is, an' now ye want till taurmint dthe very sowl iv innacence dthat Oi wus dthe manes iv procurrin' fur the ristorashun iv mae good masther's hilth. Ta hill wid ye fur iver an' iver!' accompanying his remarks with a stout blow of his hard old fist.

Madam-de-Maine reeled and fell, while Joss tripped away as if nothing had happened. She hadn't assumed this position long until she felt it acutely. Half afraid to draw upon her Joss's tongue again, or the weight of his fist, she formed a resolution of revenge that held within its howling hollow the nature of a savage race. The shock brought her keenly to her sense of self, as she straightened her slim figure before the orbs of anyone would be upon her. She walked, with eyes of evil, to her room, shut herself in to brew over the future and her encounters bordering on the near past. Her strength of thought, formed in moments of daring passion, was afterwards carried out with fearless and dauntless remorse.

Night came gently on, darkened by a heavy sky.

Delina being shown to a little room, by order of Madam-de-Maine, in which stood a small bed and a sprinkling of furniture and toilet requisites, she bathed her face and hands, brushed the elegant coils of hair, some of which hung daintily on brow and neck, changed her cotton gown to one of a newer, fresher shade, and hurried to perform the duties of night-nurse. She felt sleep would never again claim place until her lover was free from danger. Her senses were stuped in anxious thought, robbing them of all Nature's demands.

Ten o'clock struck, and still Lord Gifford never awoke. His breathing became quicker as the long, weary hours rolled by; his face appeared flushed and hot, remaining in this sick state until the doctor arrived early next morning.

Madam-de-Maine sat in her room caressing her rage at the course of events. She cursed old Joss in her heart for being the instigation of all that had taken place, for being the means of Lord Gifford's state becoming known to Dr Norton so soon, and, worse than all, the return of Delina Delaney, whose existence she had learned to well-nigh forget.

As the timid movements of Delina along the polished corridor to her little room were delicately performed, an ear of burning strain to catch them welcomed their faint echo. Rising hastily, Madam-de-Maine made for Lord Gifford's room, not to enquire after his wants or health, but for an object hideous, horrifying, and revolting. Clasping steadily the murderous weapon that glittered beyond Lord Gifford's head, she glided triumphantly out of the room, enveloping it with her silken shawl. An adept in the art of handling deadly weapons, she satisfied herself it was fully charged. She sat on, without any cognisance of the flight of time, until the deep, ringing tones that escaped from the face of an adjacent church convinced her that eleven of its deep, sweet strokes proclaimed, in sober solemnity, night was steadily advancing.

Joss, who pattered about doing little odds and ends, after the servants had retired for the night, entered the stable to examine his master's favourite pony before he, too, sought sleep. This act was the finale of his everyday duties.

Madam-de-Maine's breath came and went as she heard his heavy footsteps die below. She walked into the stillness of the night, and stood for a time face to face with coal-black surroundings. Lightly moving in the direction of the stable, she heard the familiar voice of old Joss heaping praises on the dumbness of his charge. She stopped at the half-open door, looked with devilish intensity, and observed her foe stroke the silken mane with his wrinkled, rough hand, and, muttering a few words of parting pathos, turned to come away. He held in his hand a lantern, exposing his exact position. A loud report, a sudden flash, a dense smoke, and poor old Joss staggered and fell lifeless on the stable's pavement. She wrested from his hand the lantern he still firmly clutched, set it a considerable distance apart from the blood-steeped corpse of her victim. She closed his hands round the deadly weapon, with mouth upwards – to establish the fact that fiction claimed to be a case of suicide – hummed the following lines before she closed the stable door, with a voice strong and courageous:

> Lie still, thou devil! take thy rest;
>   Sleep on, thou imp of Erin, sleep,
> Steeped in the blood I've done my best
>   To scatter at thy mistress' feet.
> True to thy master here on earth,
>   False to her who hath stayed thy might;
> Lie still, old Joss, for now no more
>   Thou'lt threaten her – good-night – good-night.

Breathing an air of freedom, she stood in the night's dead darkness. The stillness was broken by a miserable wail from a neighbouring bird that haunted the churchyard trees. She had now reached the hall door that opened so lately to the touch of a fully-fledged mass of mischievous tyranny: closed to the force of a clouded murderess. The light from the yellow-shaded lamp in her room shone over her. Now and then a deep-drawn sigh escaped from her lips. Her frame sometimes shook to chorus a thirsty sob, as if she were again contemplating a similar ordeal. Eventually, however, the signs of nervousness, that now had visited her, died and withered away, and a miraculous peace, sometimes seen on the marbled faces of Roman statuary, that exhibit strongly the polished calm of revengeful rulers, rested on her features. Her thin hands she tightly clasped, as they lay in her lap, stained with the blood of her savage bravery.

The dog now barked and whined. She quickly rose,

undressed, and, burying herself in the manufacture of deft hands, whether to sleep or not she best knew.

[A jury agrees that old Joss Danvers has committed suicide 'in a moment of temporary insanity'. Dr Norton orders a change of air for Lord Gifford, who returns to Columba Castle accompanied by Delina and Madam-de-Maine. The latter, given notice of dismissal, attempts to poison Lord Gifford by lacing the ingredients of his cornflour pudding with arsenic. Delina is found guilty of attempted murder.]

from
CHAPTER TWENTY-SIX

A panic swept over the entire court, whilst Delina fell heavily against the front of the dock.

A laugh of devilish triumph lit up the features of Madam-de-Maine.

Lord Gifford groaned aloud.

Ladies became hysterical, some fainting, others weeping copiously, and nothing was heard save sobbing and wailing. One young girl named Fanny Fowler, who had been a companion of Delina's at school, died from shock as the words fell from the clerk's lips.

The sight was one never, never to be forgotten. Mothers wringing their hands in deep and groaning agony; ladies supported in the arms of their husbands; and girls screaming because their parents could not be quieted.

A deep hush prevailed as the judge pronounced the sentence.

'Delina Delaney, you have been found guilty of this horrible crime by a jury of your own countrymen, and it is piteous to see such a handsome young girl sharing part of her bright years in a convict cell. You were set apart to attend to the wants of Lord Gifford, and devote your untiring energy to his comfort. Being tempted through some motive or other to administer to him certain deadly poisons, you must now suffer the consequence.'

So affected did the judge become, in passing sentence of five years' penal servitude on her, that he shed tears, while his lips trembled violently.

Apart from creating such a scene inside the courthouse, when the verdict travelled to the ears of the anxious throng outside it was received with groans.

Madam-de-Maine after hearing the verdict rushed towards Lord Gifford, who warded her off with feeble efforts and refused to hear a single word from her foul and blackened lips.

She then proceeded to order a car to have her conveyed to Columba Castle, but not one was at her command. She was compelled to walk along the street, followed by a hooting and hissing mob, until the services of two policemen were required to have her escorted to the residence of Lord Gifford.

Delina Delaney was swiftly driven through a sorrowing crowd, who prayed with uplifted hands of the poor orphan daughter of Joe Delaney, in whose innocence they one and all were convinced. She was placed late that night in her prison cell to live these years of false imprisonment as best she could.

Lord Gifford was assisted to his carriage and borne along to Columba Castle, accompanied by Doctors Kenny and Norton and Mr Clancarty.

The long weary day was well-nigh drawing to a close, and finding the intense heat of the thronged courthouse stamp upon them its sickening hand, they watched with gladdened interest the clock's slowly creeping hands that pointed to six.

As they sat before a table laden with luxuries, to which the visitors did ample justice, Lord Gifford said:

'Thank God, this day is almost ended!'

Talking over the painful incidents of the case, Lord Gifford would remark:

'My poor innocent Delina! Heaven strengthen her to bear the crush her young hopes have experienced, and which that callous wretch has caused her! My bud of childlike innocence will now fade ere it burst into the beautiful flower I have pictured it for years! My poor, poor Delina!'

Lord Gifford drew his hot, feverish hand across his brow.

'You still believe in her innocence, then,' remarked Dr Norton, 'despite the result?'

The fiery eyes of Lord Gifford rested on him painfully as he answered:

'By heavens, yes! And so sure as we four sit here, the day will come that shall tell to you and to the world at large that my belief is founded upon fact!'

Two dogs commenced now to bark rather fiercely, each in turn. Lord Gifford rose and walked over to the window. The sky appeared an azure globe, part of its circumference bathed in a deep, broad band of brass. The sun, standing at a certain distance still above the horizon, shot glances void of sympathy or calm upon the panting Madam-de-Maine, as she quickly walked up the avenue, after dismissing her escort at the gate. Putting up his hand to shade his eyes from the sun, he said:

'Come here, Dr Norton, and tell me if this is the figure of that villain who has stained the spotless character of her I still live to adore?'

'Yes, Madam-de-Maine approaches the Castle,' replied the doctor, as his breath insistently came and went quickly.

'Send her about her business, and at once, she can't be here,' said Lord Gifford, sinking into a chair as he spake.

She had entered now the home over which she had cast such a gloom, and, waving on her to follow him, Dr Norton preceded her into the study and imparted to her the message.

'Humph, indeed, Lord Gifford never meant such intelligence to be conveyed to me! Where is he? I must see him!'

Without time for further remonstrance she soon stood face to face with Lord Gifford.

She extended to him her hand.

'Oh, my dear and good Lord Gifford, thank God you are safe with me once more. I – I – am –'

Rising to his feet with a Samson strength suddenly thrust into the weak pores of his nervous body –

'Begone from my presence you wicked woman, servant of the devil, your daily advocate! Begone, sister of sin and mother of malice! Conspiring demon! Dare to offer your bony extremity to me, or your milky words that sound as so many shots from the mouth of a death gun! Dare to take in your polluted lips the name of Him you live to damn; the name of Him you have lived to loathe! Dare to say I am safe with you! I'd sooner offer myself as a pupil at the school where the devil is the titled tool of knowledge-imparter than tolerate your loathing presence and lingo for so much as a moment.

'Begone from my presence, my home, my all; and never do I hope to meet you on this side of time! The thought of your very shadow hurts me more than I can now express, and never can be lessened until you are for ever driven from my sight!'

She stood facing him with a bold and seeming indifference, attempting at times to talk him into quiet reasoning, but all to no purpose.

Stamping his foot, until the crystal on the table chorused

his action, he again ordered her away.

She turned, walked out of the room muttering curses as she went, gathered up all her belongings, ordered them to be sent after her, and left for ever Columba Castle, to glory in the adventures of the life she resolved to lead.

[Madam-de-Maine emigrates to America, where she has some success in high society but is later exposed. On her deathbed she confesses her crimes to Lord Gifford, who has also gone to America to escape the melancholy associations of Columba Castle and Clapham Hall. She establishes Delina's innocence and reveals her own true identity.]

from
CHAPTER TWENTY-EIGHT

Not an eye was free from the visitation of Nature's dew that beheld in the face of the dying woman the revolting nature of a lost sinner's harrowing end. Her soul had fled from form and heart, and laid its spiritual image over the shuddering form of him whom she so wrongfully wronged, losing the darts of its great pain at the sweetness of his unseen thankful smile. In the tremulous shiver of the death-chamber relief glowed steadily through its windows, no one sure of the name of the departed; yet the scene touched Lord Gifford heavily with its sceptre, and left him sobbing aloud. On hearing the dying sinner's confession, he fancied the echo of her words moaned through his heart's hollow, and set it throbbing with a deep and passionate restlessness, while his mind stood centred in the solitude of the prison cell. The great void at his heart was at last filled with a lovable design, worked in golden threads of freedom, gathered from the mighty reel of confession cast from the dying mouth of a daring sinner.

For a time silence was more terrible than terrific words – pallor much greater than death's. None of the spectators were more spell-bound than he who felt deceived to the very last.

The first who summoned courage to speak was Mr Broadbent Buick, who held in his hand the infant warrant for the release of Lord Gifford's lover.

'Lord Gifford,' he said, still trembling from the effects of the awful death he never again hoped to see sistered, 'have you reason to believe these words I've penned are true?'

Totally overcome at the force of the woman's words, he replied:

'I can scarcely credit that this corpse is that of Lady Mattie Maynard, my cousin, unless I am further convinced.'

Moving over to the bedside of death, he asked the doctor to uncover her neck. On its left side lay a round dark mark he chanced to observe while she resided at Columba Castle, and ordering her right foot to be likewise shown him, he exclaimed:

'O God, it is true! This is my cousin, Lady Mattie Maynard! She had six toes on her right foot!'

A LITTLE BELGIAN ORPHAN

Daddy was a Belgian and so was Mammy too,
And why I'm now in Larne I want to tell to you:
Daddy was a soldier and fought his level best
For both his King and Country, and I'll tell you the rest.
Our home was snug and cosy and how happy we were all,
Until Daddy he was ordered to obey his country's call;
I can ne'er forget that morning he first set out to fight,
How he kissed us all, and Mother too, and bade us do
        what's right.

Of brothers there were four and sisters just the same,
The baby sat on Mother's knee, her name was Elmo Jaine;
A tiny blue-eyed darling, with hair a virgin white
That hung in glistening ringlets, which made her look so bright;
As Daddy closed the cottage door we all burst out and cried,
Poor Mammy wrung her thin white hands, while I stood by her
        side.
'Don't cry, dear Mammy! Daddy soon will cut the Germans
        down,
And prove himself a soldier under the Belgian crown.'

One day a short time after, a troop of Germans came,
While we sat round the table, playing a childish game;
Mammy was busy baking bread for all our tea,
When the door was flung wide open and in stepped Germans
        three.
One spoke to Mammy saying, 'Stay your labour for your kids,
Give to us all this bread! or, we'll stab your bony ribs!'
And raising high his glittering sword one cut off Mammy's head,
Her body fell upon me, while her poor neck bled and bled!

Three shots soon followed after, and my dear wee brothers three
Fell dead across poor Mammy whose neck bled on my knee;
I screamed, 'Oh sirs, wee Hors is shot, and Buhn and Wilhelm
        too!'
Then on my knees I fell and begged they'd spare wee brother Dhu;

Just then they raised the little lad and threw him on the fire,
And wreathed in smiles they watched him burn until he did
    expire;
My poor wee sisters screamed and cried, and clutched dead
    Mammy's hands,
When lo! they cut off baby's head and also her wee hands.

These two sweet little sisters with fright fell on the floor,
They wailed in infant snatches, for their poor wee hearts were
    sore;
One screamed out, 'Daddy, Daddy, come home dear Daddy, do,
And kill these bad, bad Germans, or they will kill us too!'
They thrust their swords right through their eyes and tiny hearts
    as well
And gazing on their slaughter, with globes that flamed like hell,
They muttered to each other, then pulled from Mammy's hands
Two golden rings my Daddy brought to her from foreign lands.

Then plundering Mammy's meagre stores, they filled their
    knapsacks full,
And turning towards the cottage door they placed me on a stool;
'Now, kiddie girl, we'll leave you here to watch your
    slaughtered lot,
And if you move till we come back, we'll kill you on the spot.'
I raised my hands all red with blood that flowed from Mammy
    dear,
'Ah sirs,' I begged, 'just kill me now, else I shall die with fear.
I want to go along with them to live with God on high,
So kill me now, you wicked men, I'm not afraid to die!'

One drew his sword – cut off my hand, I reached the other out,
'Cut this off too, ye cowards?' I then began to shout.
In rushed some neighbour women with knives both bright and
    sharp
And stabbed the Kaiser's butchers into their very hearts.
I swooned away and nothing more remembered I since then,
Until one morning I awoke in the arms of a friend;

And glad I am I still exist to tell the world my tale
Of the half-mad Kaiser's murdering flock whose acts I still bewail.

Take warning all ye British Boys, turn out in thousands strong;
Go fight for King and Country and France will aid you on!
The Czar will fortify your troops by millions of his squad,
And if you want our Belgians brave, they'll every one be glad.
Go meet the foe undaunted, they're rotten cowards all,
Present to them the bayonet — they totter and they fall.
If you should meet the Kaiser, cut off his only arm,
For his 'wee one', it won't matter, it can't do any harm.

I've just heard Daddy, too, is killed, so all alone I'm left,
Of brothers, sisters, parents dear, I have been made bereft;
But I am not the only one in Belgium's lovely land
Who has been tortured savagely by Wilhelm's 'brute' command.
Some day I'll die and meet them all, 'twill be a joyous sight,
For us to live in glory and view the Kaiser's plight —
Tortured with remorseful flames, he won't have power to quell
If nobody conquer him on earth the devil will in ——.

from
HELEN HUDDLESON

[Helen Huddleson, the 'beauty of Ballynahinch' who is in love with Maurice Munro, is forced into a marriage with Munro's unscrupulous 'friend' Lord Raspberry. She flees from him in the company of a mysterious woman in black who seems to have taken pity on her. The woman is Madam Pear, proprietress of a brothel in a Belfast suburb.]

from
CHAPTER NINE

She knew all the forms of vice to which the human flesh and mind are heir and to continue a career of evil she bought Modesty Manor, adopting the nom-de-guerre of Pear. It was soon visited by all the swanks of seekdom within comfortable range of her rifling rooms of ruse and robbery, degradation and dodgery.

She had a swell staff of sweet-faced helpers swathed in stratagem, whose members and garments glowed with the lust of the loose, sparkled with the tears of the tortured, shone with the sunlight of bribery, dangled with the diamonds of distrust, slashed with sapphires of scandal and rubies wrested from the dainty persons of the pure.

Always on the alert for attractive magnets whose characters had still to be moulded by artful manoeuvres, she found the rosy little rural ruby, Helen Huddleson, would add considerably in advocating her accursed object. With this thought haunting her she had succeeded so far by intriguing Helen to her house of dissipation, damnation, disorder and distrust.

After capturing her apt prey, Madam Pear considered Lord Raspberry in a state of oblivion as he stood at the brougham awaiting his wife to join him. What must have been his thoughts when he failed finding her? Every face that flitted past where he stood in deep dismay, he carefully scrutinised but that of his treacherously-wedded wife was blanked from his observation. Instinct at once prompted him she had fled. He summoned one of the platform porters whose fat face was quite familiar to him. Touching the peak of his cap, Lord Raspberry enquired whether or not he had seen a young lady, at the same time describing her appearance and apparel.

'Well, sir,' said Porter Jamie, 'I couldn't say I saw her but I watched an oul' blade whiskin' a wee lassie away with her in a red hat and coverin' her with a shawl and both got into a cab and went off.'

'What was she like, the woman who took charge of the young lady?' heaving a great sigh as he queried Porter Jamie in whom the travelling public implicitly confided, being an old and trustworthy servant of the company.

'Well, sir, she looked as if she was a widda.'

'Was the lady tall, pray?'

'Long and thin,' replied Porter Jamie.

Grasping a truck and wheeling it hurriedly away, Lord Raspberry exclaimed 'Halloo', and the porter returning, he placed a sovereign in his hand. Choked with gratitude, Porter Jamie couldn't speak and, raising his cap, went smilingly away.

Lighting a long cigar to cool his nerves, the driver of a vehicle drove up and was asked by Lord Raspberry:

'Could you tell me the names of those who had cabs here tonight please?'

'I'm the boy can tell you that,' the cabman replied. 'There was Joe Cherry, Billy Burley and meself. Burley picked up a couple of weemin and went off.'

'Do you know where he lives?' spake Lord Raspberry in melancholy tones.

'I do,' said the cabman, 'but if you wait another minit or two he'll be back.'

At last Burley arrived and Lord Raspberry addressed him.

'You drove a friend of mine just now. Where – may I ask?'

'How much will you give me if I tell?' said Burley in a bragging fashion.

Lord Raspberry dropped a gold coin in his hand and the cabman whispered.

'Everybody used to call it Modesty Manor, but it has another name now which nobody can pronounce.'

Throwing away the half-smoked cigar, Burley went off for another outing, Lord Raspberry hailed another cab and was driven hastily off.

On arriving at his destination, he instructed the man to await his return. Then ascending excitedly step by step until reaching the beautifully-kept grounds surrounding his iniquitous wing of Hades during days he now damned he had tracked so often, desirous to expel from the region of his remembrance the thoughts that thrashed his weary brain with the lash of lewdness, concealing himself behind a fat chestnut tree that rose in overgrown majesty within the grounds, he resolved to rest within its massive trunk for a short time until his anger subsided somewhat.

As the moments fled, his mind became more and more disturbed lest she whom he sought might be singled out by the artful Madam to gratify the desire of some of the associates who had accompanied him long ago to her quarters of quell in quest of such innocent victims as she whose righteous robes still hung about her unsullied and free from the stamp of passion's profligacy.

Ruminating over the day's adventures as he leant against

the strong stout body of the chestnut tree, whose leafy expanding members acted in umbrella fashion to ward off tear-drops of a million sighs as they fell in thick profusion upon the verdant surface – his anger increased rather than reduced.

Never before did his actions of dishonour stand so prominently as then: how he reflected on the bitter past with all its hideous associations. Now he stood supported by the strong giant he so often before had hugged because of its silence, its secrecy, its shade, trembling in every nerve lest the virtue his loved-one claimed would pass for ever from his crafty capture to that of some equally depraved digit of distrust and distinction.

That she whom he stole from the straight and narrow path upon which she unquestionably trod was now about to walk on the crooked and broad road of destruction, driven thither by his daring desire to stab the life of his chum, Maurice Munro, with the steel of distrust in order to gratify his licentiousness by the purity of his stolen, enforced prey distressed him even to the edge of distraction.

From past experience he well knew that no gem of nature, sparkling with that rare triumphant beauty none but the true, the most pure possess, could retain chastity under the sway of Madam Pear's stained sceptre and never hitherto had this great truth presented itself to him so vividly, so strikingly.

For every finger of his filthy hands, every toe of his treacherous feet, he as often had robbed the dainty daughters of distinction, the elegant heiresses of wealth untold, the brunettes of brother dignities, the pretending daughters of saintly divines, down to the most modest maids-of-all-words, priceless pearls neither money nor prayers could ever reset.

The theft of such a character-coral he, in his moments of passion abstracted from the sacred store-rooms of his victims never taxed for a moment his designing brain with one thought of wrong or pity until he stood supporting himself against this leafy queen that so often had hid him from the eyes of the many patrolling profligates who patronisingly paced past him on their way to the seductive sanctum of searching sham, scandal and sin.

''Twas all very well,' he meditated, 'to treat as trifling the voluptuousness of youth – manhood – middle-age – inasmuch as they satisfied for the time being the greed of a "grade" passion that so often determines the downfall of the duped daughters of Eve where love was non-existent, but HE LOVED HELEN HUDDLESON with a difference, a real love for the express reason she was innocent of the wicked, wily ways of womankind.'

He had found her faithful to his chum. She told him so in her undisguised way she loved Maurice Munro, which proved a strong point to convince him of her candour, her sincerity, her loyalty to the great king – TRUTH.

And in a certain sense and as a general rule where truth prevails in either sex, in fact even in the sexless, scorn for evil in its most meagre form is in the ascendant.

Gazing intently at every window to obtain a faint glimpse of her who was torn from his protection by the vicious Madam Pear, he failed to observe the faintest reflection of shadow or light within.

Often before he had taken shelter there from the scrutiny of the corrupters who frequented this den of demoralising damndom. At times he had been admitted and emitted by means of a long French window that opened out of the bedroom, occupied at the moment by her he sought, into a small square protected by high iron railings which led to a winding staircase that served as an escape. A thick mist formed around him when lo through its compressed blur 'God' escaped from his lips. He pressed his forehead with his hand, large drops of agony sitting mercilessly thereon. Again he gazed through the dense veil of feathery foam and cried:

'What! Merciful Master! My Helen! My very own! I see you and that disreputable digit of destruction leading you, my precious pearl, my wife, into the very bedroom set apart as a seal that all therein is virtuous before corruption. Set apart as a bank in which fabulous sums have been deposited for its hire, wherein the victims sell their chastity to appease the blackguards who too often patronise its precincts.'

Moving hurriedly away, Lord Raspberry ascended the winding steps that led to this window, peeped through, saw the flaxen-haired figure of Madam Pear bend over the silk form of his girl-wife, causing her polluted lips to collide slightly with those of her innocent, artless prey, then drawing a heavy tapestry curtain across, she, presumably, vacated the room.

Lord Raspberry's heart leaped in ragged form and, tottering against the iron rails, he grasped them with a greedy grip, groaning gravely. Dread seizing him, a thousand thoughts thronged his heaving breast. At last broken sobs reached his ears, growing weaker and weaker until sleep, possibly, acted as a silent substitute. Then the room was plunged into darkness.

Lord Raspberry breathed the oxygen of artifice, sniffed the smoke of suspicion, exhaled the acid of anxiety as he stood resolving his scheme.

'Action – action – I must act now,' he murmured in breathless haste, then drawing from his vest pocket a penknife, opened the window as he had so often done before.

On entering he found himself confronted in his pyjamas by Sir Peter Plum, a mourning light exhibiting itself issuing from the next room.

Instantly Lord Raspberry struck Sir Peter who staggered and fell moaning on the softly carpeted floor.

Rushing from her boudoir, Madam Pear soon entered followed by one of her harlot litter bearing a small copper lamp whose light too was carefully subdued by a dark green silken shade with lace of the same hue.

Gazing upon Lord Raspberry who stood bleached, then on the victim of his jealous wrath as he lay in agony, blood streaming from mouth and nose, Madam Pear seemed paralysed at the mysterious presence of him who husbanded her now lying across the bed he loved, dressed as when he made her his wife not so many hours before.

'Devil! Fiend!' Lord Raspberry gasped. 'That is my wife, there in your bed of fornication covered with its deftly-marked shams of purity instead of sheets of carmine blistered with shame. Only in the nick of time have I saved her from polluting her person by the foul act of that profound puppy who lies now breathing the fumes of the wrath of him, he by his damning achievement would betray and bereave.'

Stamping his foot, Madam Pear listened aghast as he went on:

'I curse you from my heart and I curse myself I ever knew you.'

Moving over where she stood, a string of fear as seen by the twitching of her well-formed frame, he shook her sharply.

'Madam. How dare you? I say – how dare you? You have dragged my poor innocent dove – my wife – my angel into your seething saloon of sin and shame, to rob her of all the charm and grace and place her in the singed list of the loose to be in Co. with your train of degraded elegance. Give me my little rural ruby set in the folds of innocence she wears, whose mind is as pure as the balm of heaven, within whose breasts sin hath never concealed itself. I say – give her me with a robe of rags, a mind of modesty, a heart of horror for all things unclean and hands untainted by the gruesome grasp of vice, rather than a princess – a duchess – a countess

— a mimicking madonna decked with diamonds the purest, rubies the rarest, pearls of matchless lustre (produced by mechanical and mischievous means) and the defiled non-trappings some of our ugly-faced have-you-believe cream of aristocracy don to impersonate heaven's purest virgin of Babylonian blood and bearing, thereby aiming to achieve what is disgusting in the all-vacillating team of kindred humanity. I say, Madam, give me my wife rather than all these sistered as aforesaid mentioned!'

With Helen Huddleson still inert, Sir Peter Plum was being bent over by Madam Pear and her harlot help. As he lay prostrate on the carpet, Lord Raspberry continued:

'I myself,' large sweat drops falling from his brow, 'have erred within this very room. I have parred this domain ere now by bowing to a passion your presence aroused and, owing to the fallen members of humanity maimed under your unchaste roof by blackguarded blows from myself, I reflect upon the past with loathing and resolved to restore my good name by coupling it with virtue, truth and purity. And Madam, once you found out my scheme which you well knew would prove a financial asset in your future, by your designing you thwarted it in order to still continue in the diabolical role of a regardless past. I ask forgiveness for all my folly, likewise her I have rescued from the brutish and slovenly embrace of him who now lies at your feet.'

Turning to the woman who still held the small lamp with snow-white hand, who trembled clumsily at the force of his words, his face blanched.

'Never! Ah, never!' he exclaimed.

He saw in her person, acting in the capacity of a menial, the wife of a lawyer he once knew.

'Madam,' he uttered, 'how sorry I am to see you here. Have you likewise fallen? Pray tell me?'

She did not reply.

'Poor Mrs Strawberry. Poor Mrs Strawberry,' Lord Raspberry said.

The lamp dropped from Mrs Strawberry's hand, its contents falling over the face and body of Sir Peter Plum, converting him immediately into a torch of flame. Pulling him by the feet, then rushing for water to subdue the flame, dragging him into the corridor, pouring it mercilessly over him, Lord Raspberry remained until he mastered it but not before it had worked havoc on both his face and body.

CHAPTER TEN

Helen Huddleson awoke. Her power of perception seemed cleansed for ever from that dull deadly dew which hitherto blinded her, as mist from a mountain top, during these hours of despair she so recently had passed through. Alert now to all that was going on around her, her planning organ did not fail her in this her hour of blatant betrayal.

While Lord Raspberry was doing the 'brigade-man' on Sir Peter Plum, Helen, with her little satchel on her arm, was hurrying down the stair of escape, along the pebbled path so recently trodden on by him who, a few moments before, had shuddered over its shifting surface.

Out into the darkness, then passing through a gate, she ran along, led by the lighted lamps stuck against huge posts whose lights glimmered darkly against a wealth of trees. Two great pillars, with a large iron gate hanging on each, next met her view, a bright light with a globe of dull green surrounding each top. She turned towards the gate to move up the avenue but it was locked. Inside to the right stood a neat little lodge, circular in form, whose door was ajar. She called at the top of her voice.

'Anyone there, please? Come, come, fast, fast.'

The door was soon flung open when a beardy man ran out asking:

'What's the matter, little lady? Have you lost your way?'

'Open, open, open the gate, dear good man,' Helen cried. 'Oh, sir, let me into your wee house. I'm a stranger here. Let me come in, sir, do, I pray you. My name is Helen Huddleson from Crow Cottage near Ballynahinch — Lord Raspberry will chase me and capture me — and — and —'

Fainting at the gate, the beardy man removed her carefully into his little abode, otherwise an infant gate-lodge. He laid her on a soft couch in the little room beside the kitchen, slipped a spoonful of brandy between her lips, which apparently seemed closed in death, then locked the door lest he whom she had mentioned and of whom she seemed in terror, might possibly find his way in.

Father Guerdo, who had come to her rescue, was a dissipated priest who once held a large stock of parishers within his tyrannical control. He was educated at a National school in the city of Dublin, receiving his final gloss at Maynooth, and like a good many more who have been registered as dispensers of divinity in disguise, was promoted to a comfortable living which he abused in many ways, drawing the censure of those in authority over him to such a degree that he was bereaved of his sinecure as one unfit to maintain the office of priesthood.

Threatening to disclose some unpleasant duties imposed on him while being initiated into the mysteries of the Roman fold, he was accordingly installed as porter at the gate-lodge attached to the Convent of St Iscariot.

Hearing footsteps approach the door, he instantly extinguished the light a small lamp cast forth, suspended by a chain from the centre of the kitchen's ceiling of polished pitch pine. By this time the sound of carriage wheels was heard, then ceased before the huge iron gate through which Helen had been so recently carried. A loud rapping was next heard at the lodge door which continued for a goodly time, then a voice rang forth.

'Porter, porter, just a moment, please. I am Lord Raspberry. Open the door, please, do.'

Father Guerdo remained obstinate and silent. After some time elapsed, retreating footsteps were heard, when the carriage wheels hurled forth bearing their load of titled trustlessness, depositing it at the Great Northern Railway Station.

A sigh of relief escaped from Father Guerdo's lips as he drew over the kitchen window a jet-black blind. Awaking from a state edging distraction, Helen's energies grew fortified more and more, strengthened by the thought that for a time at least she would be safe from duplicity and distrust.

To analyse her feelings at that moment she felt it would have been her wish to swim the Atlantic, nevertheless there was a strange sweetness mingled in her cell of sorrow. She was satisfied that one true clean mind twined her own, that he who probably sat waiting for her away in a foreign land was rejoicing that soon he would clasp her to his bosom. With this thought her reflective faculties appeared as if she had surmounted one great obstacle in order to cross over a dangerous chasm and still fight with deadly might for her honour.

Father Guerdo now opened the door and bending over her he had rescued from tyranny, he exclaimed '*Laus Deo*', clasping his hands and turning his eyes northwards. He at once saw Helen had overcome the struggle that raged within her. Gently assisting her to a comfortable armchair deeply and softly cushioned, which he used himself in moods of deep melancholy, reflecting over a dissipated past he inwardly abhorred, to allow its pages to master him so as to tear his thoughts from this beautiful vision of loveliness so rare to be seen in the path Rome would fain make you believe you must track.

Gazing at her as she sat before a fire of logs that flamed within a well-groomed grate, all thoughts of his past were buried beneath her glance. Priest though he was, and supposed to be proof against admiration either of mistress or maid, all heresy became instantly drowned in the great tide of passion that raged within him.

Although doing penance for the past seven years by acting in the capacity of lodge porter, he still felt inclined to follow the professional routine which Roman tyranny imposes on her sons of heresy, mockery and idolatry, all of which he was sworn to support once he emitted from Maynooth, carrying them with him in his reticule of thoughts.

He had obtained a promise from the bishop to be reinitiated as parish priest as soon as a suitable vacancy conveniently occurred. He had waited seven years, still there was no appointment for him. This piqued him unpardonably and now he felt a false air blow round him and was likely to still keep blowing until his expectations became dulled, his energy impaired, his desires more limited without that distinction he had been falsely led to believe pervaded parish-priestdom.

Wavering under the spell of his misfortune and excited by the beauty of the little stranger who kept nervously wringing her hands, he asked her to give him a meagre narrative of the day's events and her reason for seeking his timely succour, which when ended he wept as never before. Her confidence in disclosing him the horror that still haunted her made him more anxious to determine her faith.

'What persuasion are you?' he asked, his voice sounding softly.

'I am a Presbyterian,' Helen Huddleson answered, 'and worship in Third Ballynahinch Presbyterian Church, once sitting under the late Reverend John Davis, a great and good man.'

Father Guerdo's face darkened somewhat, his thin lips parted, exposing two rows of irregularly-set yellow-usefuls, while he drew down his brow, instantly impressing her by the fact that he felt displeased.

'In what county,' he enquired, 'did this divine try to instruct you on matters relating to your soul's welfare?'

'In County Down, sir,' replied Helen in a nervous strain.

'Say Father, please, when addressing me,' spake he in a grim, imposing manner.

'Oh, no, no, no,' Helen answered, 'I can't call you "Father" at all, at all. I was never taught to call anybody "Father", but my own dear parent, Peter Huddleson of Crow Cottage, about a mile outside Ballynahinch, near the graveyard, sir.'

'"Father", please, when addressing me,' speaking in a remonstrating tone.

'Are you a priest, then?' Helen queried, her eyes glaring at his, burning with a fierce glow.

'I AM a priest,' he naïvely replied in a low voice.

'And what is your name, please, sir?'

'Father Guerdo,' he answered quickly.

'Then why are you living in this wee place? I thought all priests had big houses like they have in Ballynahinch.'

A sarcastic smile crept swiftly over his features.

'What a monstrous pity,' he said, 'to see a nice modest girl such as you and so beautiful, I must add, walking on the broad road to destruction instead of on the narrow path that leadeth to life everlasting. You say you are a Presbyterian. Then you are a lost sinner. No one on earth is saved from everlasting fire, only those who belong to the one and only church and that is the Roman Catholic. All others are mere shams whose worshippers pair off in small sections here and there throughout the world, every section adopting a different name, no two of which agree in principle. But, my dear girl, they will find out on the great Day of Judgment that the Roman Catholic religion was the true and only means by which all mankind could rest for ever in the angelic Mansions of Eternal Glory.

'This, I ask you: what will you think when you see your father and mother and alas yourself all branded as subjects of sin and told to move down to Hell, there to remain in everlasting punishment and torment, while the Roman Catholics will all be in Heaven singing carols along with the other angels all day long (for there is no night there) and peeking upon you and your father and mother roasting, I say ROASTING, in an eternal region of flame?'

Helen's face darkened, a choking seemed to grasp her throat with a deadly grip. She closed her eyes, clasped her hands, her pale lips moving as she prayed in low fervent tones tinged with that modest vehemence a distressed and anxious mind alone can master. Her prayer ended, she opened her eyes, fixing them steadily on the priest.

'You have been praying,' he observed, tightening his bereaved upper lip.

'Yes,' replied Helen. 'I was taught from infancy to pray when in doubt or dread.'

'Who taught you to pray, may I enquire?' asked Father Guerdo, his large dark eyes closed, his long black lashes reposing uncomfortably on his inflamed cheeks.

'The Reverend John Davis DD, of Third Ballynahinch Presbyterian Church,' Helen answered, 'who baptised me and my dear father and mother. He took the palm for offering up prayer.'

'Let it be said here,' she continued, 'that no clergyman occupying a pulpit throughout the British Isles could toe the line with him at offering up prayer. He had no rival during his day for expounding holy scripture and stood as the brightest gem in the crown of gospeldom. He was different from the majority of holy-tooters who swim round the hives of humanity at the present day. He never earned a shilling he didn't work for hard and he instructed his beloved flock more for a shilling than the clergy of today would for a hundred pounds.'

Father Guerdo observed a stern silence as she continued:

'It is patent to me, sir, that the present-day expounders of religion are merely a clique of unholy stockbrokers, acting as financial props to safeguard their own comforts than as divine messengers whose duty it is to gather the fallen of their flocks, endeavouring therefore to use every artifice within their combined power to draw them back to heavenly tutelage.'

Helen eyed him impatiently, lifting her little sailor hat and satchel, readying herself to move on to some proper shelter for the night.

'My dear girl,' said Father Guerdo, 'sit down. You must remain where you are for the night at any rate. I have but one bed, nevertheless, I'll gladly share it with you, as no harm can befall you while you remain under the roof of a chosen disciple of the Pope.'

'No, no, sir,' Helen said stubbornly. 'I have never been absent from my dear home at Crow Cottage where I was born. I can sleep tonight beneath one of those large trees bordering the south of your window blind.'

Putting on her little sailor hat, Father Guerdo stood facing the rustic ruby, then moved forward and locked the door of his menial ménage of misery. . .

from

POEMS OF PUNCTURE

JAMIE JARR

Here lies a blooming rascal,
    Once known as Jamie Jarr;
A lawyer of the lowest type,
    Who loved your name to char.
Of clownish ways and manners,
    He aped at speaking fine,
Which proved as awkward to him
    As drawing-room to swine.

I stood while the ground was hollowed
    To admit this pile of stink;
They placed the coffin upside down
    (The men upon the brink).
How the stony mould did thunder
    Upon the coffin's rump,
The louder grew the rattle,
    The deeper Jamie sunk.

His mouth now shut for ever,
    His lying tongue now stark –
His 'paws' lie still, and nevermore
    Can stab you in the dark.
Earth is by far the richer,
    Hell – one boarder more –
Heaven rejoices to be free
    From such a legal 'bore'.

EPITAPH ON LARGEBONES — THE LAWYER

Beneath me here in stinking clumps
Lies Lawyer Largebones, all in lumps;
A rotten mass of clockholed clay,
Which grows more honeycombed each day.
See how the rats have scratched his face?
Now so unlike the human race;
I very much regret *I* can't
Assist them in their eager 'bent'.

PO — THE LAWYER

Of all the names within my knowledge
E'er enrolled at school or college,
The ugliest and most obscene
Is Po — The Lawyer of Cackle-Green.

To call a man by such a name,
Especially one who apes at fame,
Is styling human nature low
By giving it the name of Po!

From humblest cot to proudest castle,
Po we call the dirtiest vessel,
Out this thought you couldn't blink
That Po's another name for — stink!

Now Po would tell you 'tis superior,
Calling —— by name 'posterior',
And why he doesn't alter Po
To Chamber — damn me if I know!

MRS ROS
AND
D.B. WYNDHAM LEWIS

MEET IRENE

by

D.B. WYNDHAM LEWIS

One has to be careful about this fine book. Some years ago, when the first edition was published in Belfast, Mr Barry Pain allowed his joy to get the better of his discretion, and retribution was swift. '*This so-called Barry Pain,*' wrote the indignant authoress, beginning a commination of the most fearful description. . .

The admirable Nonesuch Press, which prints such beautiful editions of the classics, has just issued 'Irene Iddesleigh' in a charming *format,* with three of the original wood engravings by Mr W.M.R. Quick. I am going to be extremely careful about this superb book. I am going to begin by warmly but judiciously praising the picture on page 49, which is a portrait of Sir John Dunfern, a Baronet accustomed to peruse the evening papers with 'his accustomed grace'. We see Sir John at the moment when he is exclaiming to his bride:

'Speak! Irene! Wife! Woman! Do not sit in silence and allow the blood that now boils in my veins to ooze through cavities of unrestrained passion and trickle down to drench me with its crimson hue!

'Speak, I implore you, for my sake, and act no more the deceitful Duchess of Nanté, who, when taken to task by the great Napoleon for refusing to dance with him at a State ball, replied "You honoured me too highly" – acting the hypocrite to his very face. Are you doing likewise?'

Here, I observe from the text, Sir John, whose flushed face, swollen temples and fiery looks were the image of indignation, restlessly awaited her reply. I see from the illustration that in his agony Sir John has allowed his trousers to sag. One hand is clutching his whiskers, the other grasps the back of a plush armchair. I presume that he has been tearing wildly at his braces. In the year 1897, recollect, Baronets wore their trousers baggy. Sir John's are simply incredible.

Reflection. Perhaps his wife grew cold to him on this account.

We may glance briefly at another illustration. It shows Sir John extracting from his Davenport (a kind of bureau) a letter concerning the wicked tutor, Oscar Otwell, who has robbed him of his bride. Sir John's trousers are still dastardly. In his anguish he has forgotten to pull them up at the knees. His moustache is drooping a great deal. A little Macassar Oil would have improved it. His —. But you are no doubt waiting for a précis of the plot. We should most fittingly begin, perhaps, with the opening words of the authoress herself:

> 'Sympathise with me, indeed! Ah, no! Cast your sympathy on the chill waves of troubled waters; fling it on the oases of futurity; dash it against the rock of gossip; or, better still, allow it to remain within the false and faithless bosom of buried scorn!'
>
> Such were a few remarks of Irene as she paced the beach of limited freedom, alone and unprotected.

Now we can get on. The characters are:

SIR JOHN DUNFERN, of Dunfern Mansion; a man of 'forty summers, he never yet had entertained the thought of yielding up his bacheloric ideas to supplace them with others which eventually should coincide with those of a different sex.' Marries —

IRENE IDDESLEIGH, 'another beam of life's bright rays'. An able and beautiful girl. She runs away with —

OSCAR OTWELL, 'her noble and well-learned tutor', and emigrates with him to America, leaving behind her little son —

HUGH, whose bright nature 'chased away all gloomy cavities from the mind of Sir John'.

I need not say that the Baronet is well avenged. After his wife's flight with the tutor — she was one of the women who like tutors —

Sir John sent for his solicitors, and, ordering his will to be produced,

> Demanded then and there that the pen of persuasion be dipped into the ink of revenge and spread thickly along the paragraph of blood-related charity to blank the intolerable words that referred to the woman he was now convinced, beyond doubt, had braved the bridge of bigamy.

Observe in passing that in 1897 bigamy among smart people was considered a sign of ill-breeding. But wait! Irene's Oscar turns out a dirty dog. He gets a post in a public school in America, but is soon compelled to resign 'through courting too great love for the all-powerful monster of mangled might — Intemperance'. What follows is inevitable:

> With beastly force did Oscar Otwell enter Shandon Cottage on the night of his open dismissal from Waketown Public School, and rousing from sleep his wife, with monster oaths inflicted upon her strokes of abuse which time could never efface.

Oscar then drowns himself and Irene sails for England, to be discovered at Sir John's tomb by her son. 'False woman! Wicked wife! Detested mother! Bereft widow!' exclaims the young Sir Hugh. 'How darest thou set foot on the premises your chastity should have protected and secured! What wind of transparent touch must have blown its blasts of boldest bravery around your poisoned person and guided you within miles of the mansion I proudly own?'

We leave Irene in the grounds of Dilworth Castle, 'cold, stiff, and lifeless as Nero', with the Marquis of Dilworth casting stinging looks of shame on her body. Sir Hugh, I am pleased to say, 'being strongly prejudiced by a father of faultless bearing, resolved that the sharers of beauty, youth, and false love should never have the slightest catch on his affections'. And so the story ends.

* * * *

Well (to resume), it is difficult to realise the existence of trousers like that. Lovers of the illustrations to the novels of Miss Charlotte M. Yonge will remember that the Heir of Redclyffe's trousers closely resemble Sir John Dunfern's. I forget what happened to the

Heir. 'Love, alas,' says Mrs Amanda McKittrick Ros, discussing the affair of the tutor, 'when smitten with the sword of indifference, dieth soon, but once struck on the tunnelled cheek of secrecy with the hand of pity there leaves a scar of indelible intolerance, until wiped out for ever with the curative balsam of battled freedom'.

My personal feeling is that Oscar, though a drunkard and a wife-beater, *pressed his trousers under the bed,* and was for that reason irresistible to every woman who beheld him. It is curious that Carlyle, who wrote such a lot of rugged and incoherent Germanic jargon about clothes, never discovered what must have been a deciding factor in the home and foreign policy of the Victorians: their trousers. Take Gladst–. No. Take Disraeli, who had the Old English love for green velvet waistcoats, perfumed hair-oil, jewellery, and fal-lals. His canary trousers (though not the kind I should care to be seen about town in myself) were undoubtedly smooth and flowing: and everybody knows what influence he had over the Queen. The pair now preserved at Hughenden, which are venerated by the Primrose League, once a year, are proof of this. It is patent to me that Oscar Otwell's trousers insensibly gained him the ascendancy over the heart of Lady Dunfern. Her eyes rested on them with a pang of pleasure; and then, turning and seeing Sir John in the old concertinas, she felt nothing but scorn. She then committed bigamy.

Another reason why 'Irene Iddesleigh' is a better book than 'Lord Raingo' – I am still praising this book, observe – is that it has far more exclamation marks. It is also a better book than 'The Outline of History', 'May Fair', 'Some Reactions of Colloidal Protozoids', and 'The Chartered Accountants' Year Book for 1926'. I first read it very lovingly in 1914, and almost immediately afterwards was called upon to fight. It will live. In a few years scholars will quarrel over its text, collating, comparing, indexing, and being generally tiresome. In the year 1936 Mr Tipplegrape will write a long authoritative critical study of it for the *London Apollo*; but till then, I say, it will undoubtedly live.

[*St Scandalbags*, edited with notes by T. Stanley Mercer, The Merle Press, 1954]

ST SCANDALBAGS

by

MRS AMANDA M. ROS

Under the long and honoured and peaceful reign of our Good and Gracious and Peace-loving Queen Victoria; stirring and many and multitudinous were the events, fashions and effronteries that happened, were formed and committed throughout the realms of her August Control. But, all these events, fashions and effronteries were as a midge on a camel's back, to the stale spuings, the ungrammatical effortless efforts of a 'criticising crowdrop' to be found bespattering a column – a *whole* column! (with not even a *bite* out of it) of that celestial-like-celebrated-talent-tarnisher and by name 'The Daily Mail' which one may perchance grasp –

At the Sign of the Blue Moon
Meet St Scandalbags

on 17th November 1926. I must be careful about this Saint divine. One has got to be 'purteekler' about this 'Crowdrop's Droppings'. Altho' he isn't what you'd call a 'larned feller', isn't what you'd term grammarised, yet he makes a shift to impress the public that he has at least swallowed a page or two of 'Crone's Causticiser', cremated, the ashes of which help a little to cement the 'cracked spots' within a soft brain.

Happened did it that one day away in the distance of decades, I wrote a novel which St Scandalbags describes in 'The Daily Mail' (date-year-up-yonder) as 'Irene Iddesleigh' of which he seems to chew the cud of grief he isn't the famous author!

Nor is it beyond a dram of doubt that 'Irene' must inevitably possess the art, the *undoubted art* of arousing the passions of, not alone St Scandalbags, but, of the whole character-clipping-combination including its creamiest genius-beetlers to an uncontrollable degree — as the dogs on the street — while *she* still lives to *fool* them and *force* them through capes of comparison and on rocks of revenge.

So St Scandalbags, labouring under an exhaustive dose of jalap and spite, tries, within the areas of his threadbare knowledge, to criticise a work by introducing blackguardly remarks throughout, gluing his outbursts of slum slang, always frothing with bawdy beads of banter, with a tissue of contemptible untruths which not alone are cast forth to blot the Author's fame that all the wasps in the 'trade' couldn't deface, no matter how *forceful* the sting, but to hurl his blackguardly insinuations against the character of our late ever-lamented Queen Victoria in conjunction with one of our late Parliamentary Pillars of Politics is, I would say, the most hellish of a hell-deserving calumniator!

If St Scandalbags assumes the very 'polite' role of beautifying or blemishing a Work, why not confine himself to that Work? to the point at issue? by either stamping its pages with the balm of bravery, the pulse of praise, the tincture of truth? or slashing them with the razor of ridicule, the sword of sarcasm, the pen of prejudice? But no! His arrogation to enforce his erratic vulgar services, by aiming at instructing an educated public on the subject or object matter of a Work that has stood the test of wild appreciation from all parts of the globe for a period of 30 years on its own merits alone, seems more the crowings of a cox-comb, the dross of definition and at the end of all these years the Work is a greater favourite amongst its aristocratic admirers by twenty times one.

Financially it has gone up in leaps and, having made its obeisance before the World's most select, it now takes its place as a 'Classic', thus endowing it with a gilded warrant to enter the most secret chambers of the intellect, the most sacred shelves of the divine, standing proudly amongst the bravest and most brilliant works that thought is capable of prompting, though these too have been stabbed by the scandalising sword of uncouth criticism. But woe unto me 'if I allow my joy to over-ride my discretion'.

Again it is evident that St Scandalbags doesn't believe in method. Possibly manners plus method seemed not in force within his infant domain, as very often folks' adultisms are the reflections of their infantisms, hence his erratic efforts to try to pen the merits or de-merits of this wonderful 'nerve-disturber', as seen in 'The Daily Mail', Nov. 17th. 1926.

PARAGRAPH 1

Throughout this para', twig how bilious St Scandalbags grows over a retort of the Author, made years back by ten times three (and to be found within the Primus Pages of 'Delina Delaney' by the same Author) to his brother Brain-buster in common – Barry Pain – another talent wiper of a wormy order, or so-called critic if you will.

How masonic is 'de feller sidin' wid' 'Barry! and to emphasise his undying love for Barry, he swears he will denounce 'The Book of the Century' beyond recognition by the introduction of black-guardly insinuations and untruths of the most infamous kind which go to prove an ambition from which chimney-sweeps would shrink and coal-heavers abhor!

He quotes in this passage – 'Lately, I believe a similar scourging awaited an incautious publisher who wanted to include 'Irene Iddesleigh' in a series of the World's Worst Novels'!!!

This is a deliberate and brazen-faced lie, solely formed and fashioned within the low vulgar mind of St Scandalbags, as no publisher – cautious or *in*cautious – ever wrote me on the subject directly or *in*directly, therefore, apart from penning such a dastardly untruth (the outcome of a 'low dirty dog') he wrote this treacherously-tainted conglomeration of libellous and licentious fiction prompted by the smoked spirit of vindictive villainy for the sole purpose of defaming my work and to make good his onerous oath when crushing himself into the 'holy' craft of genius-scathers.

PARAGRAPH 2

Jealousy – Ignorance – Irony I pass over.

In this para', see how artistically, how divinely, how beautifully St Scandalbags depicts an illustration, three of which have been introduced within the pages of this book by a hewer of wood in the person of W.M.R. Quick, who likewise comes under the 'mellowy' pen of this exegetical branch of the 'fine arts'! His remarks in this paragraph portray the fact that his perceptivity is a bit punctured.

He must have dwelt on this illustration meagrely, otherwise his 'artistic' stars strain sorrowfully.

He alleges Sir John Dunfern clutches what he never *had*! with one hand which likewise gives forth the lie direct, as this hand clutches nothing, is quite open and doesn't appear desirous to court acquaintance with what he is bereft of at all! while the other, he intimates, 'grasps the back of a plush armchair'!

These remarks either define his ignorant grasp of the 'fine arts' or go to prove emphatically his orbs are on holiday, for I hold it isn't a chair at all! armed or *un*armed, neither gowned in plush nor any other such fabric.

What if his wandering thoughts carry him back to his old granny's kitchen! whose roof perchance was covered with, it may be, 'tarred felt' or a Saxon Shawl of battered straw and scolloped about its south with little osier rods in order to keep the ends down and in proper subjection, lest a high wind would expose it uncomfortably to the detriment of the old woman within, thereby drawing comment from a gazing public ever eager to see a mote in the eye of a foe or a dinge in their neighbour's wee thatched shanty.

Reverting once more to the 'plush armchair' which suffers severely at being mis-called.

An inartistic eye would never be guilty of gazing towards it at all, in fact, wouldn't tax it looking therewards, for giving it a level look, the old 'jumbo' seems more in harmony with the scrags of an old 'settlebed' that has been cast for ever from the wee smoky resting-place of a back-gone fame-slasher labelled no good. But I observe, I say observe, even in *face* of being thus labelled, how quickly Quick's rustic eye beheld it, end up one fine day, date unknown, in an ancient bog-hole after a torrential downpour had ruthlessly swept away its turfy wrappings; thereby exposing its strong parts after generations of woe and misery. I say, Quick's eye and quicker action hacks 'ims' up into such clever pieces as to gull the fellow who nicknames it 'A Plush Armchair' plus a 'wood-engraving'!

What a stirring capacity this 'larned feller' possesses for baptising bits of bog-oak Dummydoms!

I make obeisance to his cleverdoms, also to the wooden artist's, with his exquisite bit of bog-oak bedisms.

Towards the end of No. 3 Para', St Scandalbags seems to drift away entirely from the subject he commenced with such stirring bravo. It is lucid he seems mortally drenched in wonder *where* the food is to be formed for further demolition.

Then, as if ignored by 'Irene', who up to the present laughs unseen in her repository of calm, having proved such a wonderful magnet in the market of Belles-Letters, in a moment of mad defeat, he turns the *tail* of what *should* be talent, upside-down by introducing a subject entirely foreign to this huge 'Bowel-Disturber' as at first issued, leaving 'Irene' alone for a time until he aims at cutting the wings off the wooden artist (Quick) to be sure.

He seems itchy a bit, scratches his ——, may be excited over the jalap business, tries a further dose of laxatives and, in this wormy state, he isn't half satisfied to think the wooden artist (he is allowing 'Irene' rest for a time be it known) didn't hew Sir John a better pair of trousers that 'sagged so' a short time previous when the wearer thereof was in the horrors of agony.

Now all Christian-folk such as St Scandalbags, who is a mighty mite in a maggoty circle ('tisn't every one can toot the horn of Saint), should know and are convinced beyond a shadow of doubt, that any man – Baronet or Brain-Blighter – whose agony swells his temples, flushes his face, fires his looks, especially from a jealous cause, wouldn't under the circumstances *allow* his 'trousers' to sag at all! especially that portion which seems to be overlooked by this pessimistic prig.

Again, concerning this spicy paragraph, all of which smells so rank, so 'dastardly', recollect also that St Scandalbags refers to Sir

John's 'braces' and 'trousers' as part and parcel of a Baronet's requirements in this world of dandyisms and in the year 1897. Better to style them 'suspenders' and 'breeches', which are more in touch with the dignity of Baronets and all who tread north of this dignity's Baronial embellishments, especially those born within the thoroughfare of thought.

But for 'braces' and 'trousers' — smelling so partridge, so critic-like — these rusticised applicables are quite in order in their twindom of support and sex when worn over the drooped shoulders and crackling joints of a mushroom class of talent-twisters who mostly emit from a wee bit cabin or in fact a moderate oil-barrel quilted inside with hay or straw and 'keeled' with netting wire.

But, there *are* exceptions, too few in number, for instance — Aldous Huxley, Stafford Thackery, Edward Kenmuir, Charles Howden and that celebrated Divine, Dramatist and Critic of the highest summit, John Lyle Donaghy.

Three of these were critics of a very distinctive design, of a very high order in their day and generation, while the remaining two *were* and still *are* eminent talent-pickers, throughout this world suffering so, at the present time, from a great drought in the art of honest criticism.

Aldous Huxley and John Lyle Donaghy never prune a branch of thought until assured the trunk is tainted and the root diseased. *Then,* and *not* until *then,* they exhibit they *are* critics, fully fledged and feathered with a stock of pros and cons, carrying with them neither malice, spite nor revenge, as too many (but of quite a mushroom class) do, concerning the Works they honestly criticise. Directed by an unbiased mind, these men are altogether and wholly outside the mean circles of scribblers and scandalisers who throng our cities under the nom-de-plume of critics, some of whom it would pinch to enumerate the vowels their names bore.

Aldous Huxley and John Lyle Donaghy condemn, by a powerful demonstration, the weak, the idle drossy dirt the reading public are asked to believe is the essence of a clever brain and upon such men the educated public can implicitly rely. Mark the fact, the great fact, that 'classic' critics never allow their pens to depict their conclusions re. strong or weak forms of thought or traits of talent with the ink of ignorance, revenge or blackguardism 'macassared' over with the oil of odium as their less-endowed insignificant 'crowdrop' contemporaries do. Oh no!

<h2 style="text-align:center">PARAGRAPH 5</h2>

St Scandalbags earnestly draws the attention of his readers under the bay-window of bigamy.

He avers that this very common form of illicit love was considered 'a sign of ill-breeding amongst "smart people" of the past century'! or towards its tag-end rather.

He drops criticising altogether within the region of this sentence and assumes the role of instructor! Erratic fellow! Must again be still labouring under the jalap effects which seem to clog – no! which seems to undo! Ah, I am still thinking of the 'trouser' adornment of the Baronet! How I fly for a sniff of Paradigmatical Pharmaceutic – I say, I simply fly!

I am studying strongly whether Oscar Otwell could possibly be classed amongst the 'smart people' or the 'smart set'? I fear not, but *'Irene' was*, so St Scandalbags has merely falsified the position of the man, never mind the 'set'.

Being but a tutor, he knocked the 'smart people' into a cocked hat altogether, in point of erudition, as all livestock do who graze on the same pasture. But 'Irene', being a spoke in the wheel of gaiety, and one of the 'smart set' towards the close of the last century, doubtless rode in the same train as her 'smart' contemporaries, imitating *their* desire to ignore the bond of matrimony which bound her to a husband she grew to dislike. Hastening to a foreign land, to carry out a reverent lawless love of youth, she identified herself as a bigamist, which she, one day, grew to grieve. Groaning under a weight of woe, she repented of her past and fain would have cast herself again under the tortured 'wings' – beneath the 'baggy trousers' which St Scandalbags alleges seemed culpable for her bigamy! Ah! the miraculous modesty of this scurrilous scribe, casting upon her the saddle of cowardice and mockery that the 'smart' folks' morals may not suffer.

There isn't much to relate within these twins, save a slight stroke of unmerited honour attached to the name of Sir John Dunfern's son — Sir Hugh or, as St Scandalbags describes him — 'Lord' Hugh! Undoubtedly there is no scarcity of 'Macassar Oil' within this partial pack of scathers, nor is *he* stinted on bestowing it lavishly upon this young dignity, by 'Macassaring' him over with his unction, drenching him with the last rites of Sir, to further elevate him a few steps higher up the ladder of Christlike distinction — O Lord! What a reverting nature this 'Macassar Oil' has taken to be sure! But 'I mustn't comment — nobody could'.

What an age we doubtless live in! When scribblers of this thick-witted type can impersonate with such irreverence The Royal Sovereign by conferring titles upon his subjects, the lowbred would giggle at — the highbred scorn.

Where ignorance and arrogance attend the demise of Education, we must bid adieu to the liberal services of the Ancients.

NOTE

It is undeniably evident from first to last by his column of calumnious, scurrilous blackguardisms found in 'The Daily Mail of November 17th 1926', that St Scandalbags meant to aim at criticising, but feeling his gross inability to fathom facts, feeling his intellectual capacity wane under the excessive tumour of thorny thought with which he felt so confident to prick the pages of this magnetic mystic he, yielding up the *ghost* of criticism apparently resorts to overhaul his stock of moth-eaten literature and that of a low, rough average, in order to extract therefrom a 'something' instrumentally astounding in point of power, in order to crown the overthrow of this extraordinary literary effort on achieving its highest ambition by wearing now and for ever its 'Classic' Crown at the youthful age of three decades!

Rather disappointing isn't it, that this egotistical earth-worm, this aspiring asset in the world of conceit, has failed in his earnest endeavour to find that astonishing 'something' within his decayed box of demoralising contents, his battered trunk of wormholed sheets of sham?

'Tis such a pity, such a drop that he is so rascally thwarted from achieving the object of his *prompted* desire. Even *had* he been successful the question arises – What – would – the – result – have – been? 'A Coroner's Inquest' trampling under the heels of Death, resulting from an overdose of joy inasmuch as he had at last achieved the triumphant all others wearing 'budgets' ditto have failed in their jealous jadery to do.

But alas! There will be no Inquest, I fear, so far as his baby abilities range in the category of scathing.

It is now decades three since first this Work made its entrance into the minds of the mighty, the hearts of the righty, the disordered little brain cells of the jealous and, does it not smell strikingly strange – stranger than the birth of this book, first formed within the Vale of Valour, that during all these years, despite the flagrant fact it has more than once suffered the scores of the carving-knife that mostly lies scabbarded by two hemispheres of dentistry – with few exceptions, it has moved along modestly, steadily, beloved by the brave, clamoured for by the borrowers, despised only superficially by a cliquy cabal of the 'crowdrop' class, so accustomed to grind talent, outside their line of oratory, with the Portland pegs of jealousy, creamed to overflowing with blackguardisms and every other ism symbolical of a jealous, wicked mind, especially if the object of their spleen rise so high in the estimation of its public patronisers as to warrant it being placed upon the select shelves of the 'Classic'.

His critique ends, he grows positively sick, apparently being overcome by the fumes of the 'Macassar Oil' and then the effects of —— my! He throws down his 'quill', being blunted beyond scandalising point, pricking his foolscap and all to no purpose – (too bad – too bad) further than jingling a few 'tanners' in the pockets of his 'trousers' that look *so* dastardly, *so* bagged about the kneecaps.

Snapping up another designer of evil thoughts, some of which must be classed under a premeditated desire to defame not the Author but, the most immaculate, irreproachable Sovereign who ever graced the proud old Throne of England or that of any other nation – Queen Victoria! whom coupled with another dignity I shall deal with further along the line.

Again he resorts to chew the cud of the irresistible but, as his rambling remarks don't apply to the Author, she passes on to the next 'jargon' with its lines of lewdness.

Yet again he goes for the 'trouser' controversy.

It is within the aching area of this huge paragraph, that he excels in exposing his back-street slang.

St Scandalbags here alleges that 'a man bcreft of "trousers", or for a short cut "*pants*", is irresistible to every women who beholds him'.

This is rather a sweeping statement, too sweeping, too loose! That he possesses a voluptuous greed, as to the 'cut' and hanging propensities of this southern necessary, this attribute of adornment, disputes doubt.

That he also has a very meagre knowledge of the shy, the noble, the virtuous – and a very liberal one of the common, the lustful, the adulterous – remains a problem he can best solve.

I don't fancy formidable forms of nakedness – male or female – neither count I the faintest respect for a man posing as a critic or cadger to introduce such filthy super-blackguardly remarks towards even harlots or the drossiest drabs who inhabit the blighty Brothels of the damned.

What about the Devil, himself promoter of all evil within our limited globe, I say what about him?

When tempted by one of England's proudest and fairest daughters, did *he* kick off his 'trousers' or keep them on when this depraved daughter of the damned and to wit, wife of a millionaire, pled with him with a passion St Scandalbags would term irresistible? [The reference is to an episode in Marie Corelli's *The Sorrows of Satan*.] Nay, resolute he stood, a reprimanding magnate of the Infernal – a proud Chief over defeat, never undoing a button of his southern covering.

To be guilty of exposing himself 'trouserless' to this most immoral corrupting digit of dignity, he would scorn and yet he proved irresistible despite her marvellous passion-pleading and magnitude of appeal, therefore St Scandalbags is in error just for once! Of course there *are* exceptions to all rules within the diocese of demonstration.

Next he attacks Carlyle.

Carlyle did his duty in his day, as mostly all great writers do; he has left a record behind him but not a calumniating one. Born under the twittering star of the erratic, the silent moon of the eccentric, Carlyle pleased in his day and generation his thousands of admirers, and whose erraticisms and eccentricities carried with them a delightful, healthy humour found in few, if any, of his contemporaries.

But as is the case of many another writer, his depth of intellect was greatly misunderstood; nor was his knowledge of mankind and matters fully fathomed. Even today, a mystery clings around many of his writings which no one can ever solve, unless some one yet to be formed and fashioned as he whose manner and style will run concurrently, being propelled by the mighty engine of thought, *then* and not *until* then, shall 'Honour to whom it is due' ring triumphantly over the crumbled and hallowed bones of him (every true scholar admired from the same standpoint) who wrote such 'rugged incoherent Germanic jargon,' so sayeth St Scandalbags, who if possessed of Carlyle's brain-powers would be aiming at dethroning King George.

After stabbing the dead author, as well as the living (at least those who would bow to his sectional blarney), he proceeds to stick his glitterless bayonet ruthlessly into the relics of Queen Victoria and her trusted adviser Disraeli.

He describes the latter's 'trousers' as 'loose and flowing', adding 'that everybody knows what influence he had over the Queen'. I hold that any man, or form of man, who would border on publicly dragging two such honourable names within the vicinity of his scurrilous, blackguardly pen for circulation amongst the noble men and women who felt and feel honoured at being called subjects of one of the bravest, most brilliant, noble, honourable, moral Christian Queens who ever graced and adorned the British Throne and which now holds within its historic arms, a King and Queen (King George v and Queen Mary) equally endowed with all the ancestral virtues so exclusively reverenced by his noble and beloved power of adornment, whose memory shall live in the hearts of her honourable subjects so long as life lasts and shall be bequeathed to their posterity as a legacy of truth, virtue, love and respect, should be ostracised from society, however skim, if not already a sufferer from such effects. Is it not then one of the gravest and grossest of scandals that ever appeared or was permitted to be printed in any paper, public or private, decent or *fringed* with decency, for a man sexed or unsexed – and posing as a critic by the bye! – such as D.B. Wyndham Lewis, to proceed by a train of thought driven thither by an engine charged with the foul steam of a mind pregnant with capsules of corruption of the rottenest filthy type, to Frogmore (where this Queenly Death-Diamond of the first and purest water reposeth in her Royal Cradle of Calm, made more calm because of her cleanly and blameless life, her duty towards God and her countless subjects, her unflinching love and her rigid reverence for all things associated with a true Christian life) enter its holy portals, to view this Great and Good Queen, who lay within its hallowed walls in order to tear into scrags her chilly unstained death-robes and riddle her lifeless form with his deadly pellets of scandal?

Is there or could there be anything south of Heaven or north of Hell, more dishonourable, more degrading, more reptilic than to tarnish, with the filthiest compound a low vulgar mind is capable of inventing, the characters of the undeserving, years after they have resigned their right of existence, thus deprived of the option or power to defend themselves against such cruel calumny?

These clay-crabs of corruption, nicknamed 'critics', know, as well as life is a loan, that their lives are one crooked stream of dissimulation, dishonour, falsehood (with rare exceptions) and it is a wretched waif who would covet their 'jobbery'.

So far as Lord Beaconsfield or Disraeli – as St Scandalbags styles him – is concerned, I confess, I am not, either now or when less figures totted up my years, too particular in associating myself with foreigners so to say, and especially with those of a Jewish ancestry, prominent as murderers of our Lord and Saviour, Jesus Christ – nevertheless, 'Disraeli' I hold in conjunction with those of his political followers, as well as his scions of scandal, during his premiership, was all a gentleman in such a prominent position *should be*.

He was a man of honour, crowned by a coronet of conviction nothing could shatter and free from the most trivial trait of staining that honour either by word – deed – or in thought, during his reign as one of Queen Victoria's noble advisers. And because of his political position during the stages of his periodical premiership and which position entailed being in close touch with the Sovereign, be that person King or Queen, I say, this is no visible reason why he should be dragged throughout the corrupting columns of 'The Daily Mail' bearing date so recently as 'Nov. 17th 1926' as a man of an immoral nature towards his Sovereign!!!

For the idiotic, spiteful balderdash which goes to complete this portrayal of a thick-witted, evil-minded snapshot of spleen, of which every line within this 'foul column' seems pregnant, plus all the other excellent qualities mentioned, I'll confine to the waste-paper-basket, where its morals, let all hope, will be found to stay their bloody propensities.

Betrayed by what is false within,
    The censure of the just is thine:
I envy not your post of sin,
    I feel so proud it isn't mine.
I've solved your best – not worth a glance
    From eyes so used to scan what's true;
I've shunned the worthless, there's a chance
    You'll profit by – This gift to you.

[*St Scandalbags*, edited with notes by T. Stanley Mercer, The Merle Press, 1954]

THE ENGINEER DIVINE

Across the deep chasm which nothing can fill
Since man was from Paradise driven,
The Great Engineer with remarkable skill,
Constructed a railway to Heaven.
The Span of the Bridge is a wonder of strength
And of sightless beauty combined,
Its dimensions in breadth and ditto in length,
The Master of All hath designed.

The wires of communion, extended with care,
From Earth to the Station above,
The current of faith from the battery of prayer
Can act on the Magnet of Love.
With movements produced by a Motor Divine
Which matchless perfection displays,
The Engine of Truth as it runs up the line
The Train of Salvation conveys.

THINE IN STORM AND CALM
SOME LETTERS

8 December 1905

It has just come to my notice that you had the Tinker-like impert-
inence to send me the enclosed. Would you be surprised to know
that I don't owe Porter one cent? If not, I'm here to inform you.
What importation are you, by the bye? I thought Belfast already
stuffed with such priggish prey. And you demand my damned 2/6
for writing 'THIS' piece of toilet paper. Well, I wouldn't give you
2/6 for all the WC requisites in Belfast, and solicitors included,
mark you — for I hold that all trash emanating from such 'would
be's' fit for no other purpose, therefore I return it, inasmuch as
you presumably have as much call for it as I, thanks ARFULLY. If
such PUPS as you would mind their own business and not stick
your nose into that of a lady's, I consider that you would have
quite enough to do, and more than enough. I am quite content to
transact my own business without the intervention of such
noodles and if I were as near you now as I am to my pen, I'd give
your neck a twist you'd probably remember. Whisper — do YOU
owe anything? If so, go and pay it. Just let Mrs Ros alone, she
neither regards you nor all the bloodhounds in Britain one diluted
damn. . .

[Quoted by Jack Loudan, *O Rare Amanda!*, p. 99]

TO HER SOLICITOR

June 1907

It happened on Thursday last while I was visiting Glenoe that this
woman rushed suddenly into the house, frothing at the mouth, as
if a tigress in pursuit of prey. She flung her cap into one corner,
while her eyes kept rolling wildly, like one whose sanity demanded
questioning. Then she rushed into the street and shouted to me:
Come out, Ross, you bloody b...., for I'm d....d if I don't bog my
feet into you. . .

[Quoted by Loudan, *O Rare Amanda!*, p. 102. In 1907 Amanda undertook the management of a lime kiln and farm near Larne, the property of a friend of her husband named Crawford, who was ill. Some of Crawford's relations and neighbours resented her style of management. Loudan, p. 98ff, describes the hostilities and legal battle that ensued. The woman referred to in the letter was a neighbour.]

TO ARTHUR PONSONBY ESQ.
(I feel a higher title is yours.)

1910

My Dear Sir,

Yes, indeed, I am my own publisher and shall be to the bitter end. I don't believe in publishers who wish to butter their bannocks on both sides while they'll hardly allow an author to smell treacle. I consider they are too grabby altogether and like Methodists they love to keep the Sabbath and everything else they can lay hands upon. This is my experience of the crew.

My next work, which could not appear too soon, is written chiefly to cut up the lawyers, a gang I absolutely detest. When it appears, they will get a chance then of snarling and biting and guzzling each other in their dog beds of injustice. They'll get a tiny 'drop' when they swallow its intestines. I've thrashed the clerics too and Royalty won't laugh over its pages.

My present two works were written more through fun, but I turned the scale when writing 'Six Months in Hell'. It is as different as tar from snow. I hope when you have the pleasure of digesting its pages that you will add to its long list of expected admirers.

I am, Thine, Verily,
AMANDA ROS, AUTHOR

[Quoted in full by Lord Ponsonby in a letter to the *New Statesman and Nation*, December 1935. He had written to Amanda enquiring about a projected novel, 'Six Months in Hell'. Ponsonby, who took his seat in the House of Lords in 1930, noted that in her final comment she 'scented a peer even at the distance of twenty years'. 'Six Months in Hell' was never finished. Loudan notes that Amanda considered a number of alternative titles: 'The Lusty Lawyer', 'Rufus Ryle', 'The Hedge Round Hell', 'The Murdered Heiress', 'Denis Doghead' and 'Benjamin Bunn'. The only portion to appear in print was published by T.S. Mercer's Merle Press in 1954, under the title *Donald Dudley, The Bastard Critic*.]

TO ELIOT FITZGIBBON

2nd September 1910

My Dear Sir,

I feel sure, belonging, as you do, to the masculine gender, that you will forgive me not answering your very nice eulogistic letter, rec'd duly and which I shall treasure amongst the many thousands of which I hold.

The fact is, I am always kept so busy, having several businesses to attend to, that punctuality has almost become a step-daughter to me. I attend to business always first and hold back all correspondence re my works to be dealt with once weekly if possible and in your case I find I have held back even longer. Won't you forgive me? I could swear to your 'Yes'. (This is a little phrase contained in my present work, 'Six Months in Hell'.)

. . . As yet I have only two works published. . . and my third is in the hands of the printers. I am my own publisher, I don't believe in the usual channel of authors. In this instance I am like my works – a bit peculiar – and pride myself on being so.

My present work is very severe on law-hounds in particular and judging from your name, you likely are identified with the damning body, if so, God help your nerves unless made of iron capable of being melted or bent by the strongest hammer of sarcasm it is possible to shape – critics, clergy, editors, together with 'Society-Noodles' or 'dullies', likewise come under the flail of the thrasher.

On the whole I am delighted with this work at which I have been engaged four years and hope it will appear on the footboard of mimicry at no distant date.

I feel I am a great favourite as a writer, my fame is established which is the chief point of success. I am sending books this very day to Constantinople and Chicago, in fact I have spent *all* day sending away my works.

Lords, Ladies, Earls, Countesses and Ambassadors are my chief patronisers. In fact I hold letters concerning my works from all crowned heads except the Czar of Russia and the Emperor of Austria. I don't say this in a spirit of boasting, for I detest bombast, but that you are literary I mention it to you. You speak of my courage! Ah! you will have more cause to speak of this trait in my character when you read 'Six Months in Hell'. . .

There is a prayer contained in this book which will wring from the sourest specimen of creation the most sugary laugh in existence.

The hero is a bastard and writes poetry while in hell, but I mustn't tell too much. . .

Believe me,
My dear Sir,
Thine Verily,
AMANDA M. ROS, AUTHOR

[Quoted by Jack Loudan, *O Rare Amanda!*, pp. 93–5]

TO CAPTAIN P.R. WHALLEY

January 1911

My Dear Sir,

Your letter have I and a very nice one too, which I assure you I don't dully appreciate. It struck me forcibly and strangely (no doubt as I read your well-penned epistle), I until lately have laboured under a grave sense of error re Army officials (especially where autocratic arrogance is supposed to be a ruling and at the same time imperative feature) were a class of individuals as void of kindness or feeling as a lawyer, but lately I have been compelled to alter my opinion as really among the thousands of letters I hold concerning my works alone, the nicest, the kindliest, the friendliest effusions are from gentlemen swathed in the service of the sword. . .

I have a work presently in the Press named 'Six Months in Hell' which you may one day read. I consider it will be worth perusing, bruising badly the morals of Britain and America, while Royalty, clergy, critics, society and bloodhounds of law must all incur its censure. For my works I shall be and aye my own publisher and my books can only be had direct from myself.

Strange yet true, I have only two copies of 'Delina' in my possession now and I am sending *you* one of them in preference to all other requests lying here before me, while the other I feel bound to send to Lady Julia Duff, who wanted two. . . Lady Caroline Warren also wants another, but cannot favour her request, as 'Delina' tonight is totally exhausted.

I have written you a letter instead of a note which at first I intended, but once in a while I am in a better vogue for dashing down thoughts than others and fortunately or unfortunately I now possess that mood. I daresay most individuals are bathed with similar ingredients. . .

I am,
Very Dear Sir,
Thine in storm and calm,
AMANDA M. ROS, AUTHOR

[Quoted by Jack Loudan, *O Rare Amanda!*, pp. 55–6]

TO T.S. MERCER

21 November 1927

I am pleased to say this Work [*Irene Iddesleigh*] now rests upon the shelf of 'Classic', for which reason I presume the critics, lately, have done their utmost to murder both the Book and its Author; nevertheless I – still – live and the Book shall never die.

Their bayonets of bastard sheen with their scurrilous punctures of jealous jadery affect neither the Book nor its Author financially but, on the contrary, will not be overlooked by me, in the near future.

I consider it the most degrading vice South of Heaven or North of —— for any man or men, clique, class or cabal to squint at and pluck a gem or a thorn from out of the pages of any Book, either written to gratify or damn, without first of all dealing with every line and solving the whole as the mind dictates, whether to express their opinions or keep it wrapped up within the folds of where their brains *should* be!

I hold these would be *intelligibles* of bad-breeding before lashing into their spleen in which they seem to take such delight, should feed fully upon, at least, the husks of truth especially concerning Authors of a decent standard of life, before lashing into print their low-bred opinions of works of which they know as little as a 'Hippopotamus' knows about 'The Lord's Prayer' and for the simple reason that the brain of such is void of that perspective matter the Books freely feed, they appease their stupidity, their grasping void by denouncing the Books and Authors both, tearing into scrags those efforts which the major portion of the World admire — love and worship.

My chief object of writing *is* and always *has* been, to write if possible in a strain all my own. *This* I find is why my writings are so much sought after.

My works are all expressly my own — pleasingly peculiar, not a borrowed stroke in one of them.

I write as I feel and as I don't feel.

I please the huge army of readers I always maintain.

I afford pleasure and give satisfaction to the million and one who continually thirst for aught that drops from my pen.

Such being the case one feels happy affording others pleasure but —

The scandalmongering critics, through sheer and corrupt jealousy, largely retard the spread of unique literature by their infamous untruths concerning particularly those Novelists the World favours and until *they*, unlike the veritable martyrs of old, recant or are openly denounced and led to Tower-Hill, novelists will turn their talent in another direction.

Up to the present few critics understand my writings thoroughly.

Aldous Huxley. If you have not read his book 'On the Margin', you should purchase one in which he deals with 'Delina Delaney'. I think 'Eupheus Redivius' leads you towards his critique on this work. This book of his was sent me from London and my brother has it presently, else I'd let you have a look at it.

Lately I have felt so indignant about these adverse criticisms that I was half inclined to turn my time to matters more secret.

[The letters to T.S. Mercer reprinted here are among those he published privately, as *Bayonets of Bastard Sheen*, 1949. 'Eupheus Redivius' is, of course, 'Euphues Redivivus', Aldous Huxley's essay about Amanda in *On the Margin*.]

TO T.S. MERCER

8 December 1927

I feel you are not in love with that 'mushroom' class of 'Idiotics' so prone to condemn phraseologists for, I assure you, I don't admire their drunken modes of hacking the misunderstood.

If these denunciating 'Arabs' to be 'masonic' acted as tilers, at the doors of the imagination, or paced around the suburbs of Authors' thoughts when writing Books, they might naturally wring therefrom a 'something' that might possibly inaugurate them with the regalia of at least decency, a little of which they, occasionally in their sober moods, could flavour their bombastic, brazen attacks with.

But no! They almost all toe the same line. One man of deep thought has got to feed the ninety-nine 'weaklings' bereft of the power to think for themselves. One honest critic, few of whom exist in this World of literary differences, is prone to issue in all instances an honest opinion on every line his honest mind dictates pro or con – A man – such – is to be greatly appreciated e'en *were* his criticisms adverse.

When such a man's opinions appear, the ninety-nine grasp with a voracious greed all such, as Americans hug pirating, clique together like a band of forgers, discussing the weakest pros and cons, then pair off to make the most of honest opinion by adopting the role of scandalising, picking out different sentences and transforming them into the vilest derogatory dross about the objects of their spleen and the honourable producers of Novels!

Their damning attacks crush! and all to no purpose so far as novelists of fame are concerned, some of whom pass such criticisms or blackguardisms un-noticed, but *I* for one don't miss a bar of attack without payment in full.

I hold Editors are largely to blame for allowing their pages to be blurred and degraded past redemption by such attempts masked by a hood of jealousy, which neither bring credit to *them* nor any right-minded reader.

Suffice it to say, it is deeply to be deplored that Novelists, clever or dull, who undoubtedly do their utmost to give pleasure to the great reading public; who labour *more mentally* than any other class of creation in the World in order that such labour might serve to mitigate the sorrows of a swarming populace and afford them pleasure when too often sorrow would supplace the void, should not be protected from the corruptive, lying, self-originating dross these so-called cornerboy shadows of criticisms are permitted to offer to a well-educated public through the sheer ignorance and drastic greed of Editor-Grabbers whose duty *should* be to protect those whose calling largely clashes with their own!

I know many orthodox writers, who, within the last ten years, have thrown down their 'quills', never more to be exercised in the cultured role and it is to be deplored how scanty the output of good Novels at the present day.

Marie Corelli with all her caustic points was, I am creditably informed, driven to a premature grave through the filthy attacks both on her Work and person which were allowed to pass by the stream of contradiction, the river of retaliation, without the faintest attempt to drown them beneath the waters of scandal.

All her million and one readers stood a clinging, consolidated mass of humanity, weeping and wailing let us suppose, that a great Queen of Novelists had crossed the life-line, yet, how many of them were there who rebuked, during her honoured lifetime, the attacking mobs largely responsible for her deplored demise? I say – From all such, Good Lord deliver *me*!

Personally, as a writer, well I know my writings are wholly different from the commonplace everyday novel.

I also know I write absolutely different from any known writer or organiser of prose. I don't write in the usual novelistic, babyish manner in which the majority of other novelists do.

I write to be superficially understood by the superficial, by the poorest souls, the colour and blend of whose blood differ not an iota from that of Royalty or those sections of Society who are gradually stepping down the ladder of distinction, every step bringing them nearer and nearer to the common level, thereby veining themselves with that blood they so long have mocked and despised. Does not this fact, this present-day state of things, prove the absurdity of blood-caste in its most literal meaning?

The poor who bought their education for a sixpence, I write as well as for those who could not purchase my unfathomable ideas or workings of the mind with the millions of a Rockfeller or Stewart.

Even my peculiar manner of writing, which has brought me thousands of miscellaneous admirers (as well as the scalding few whose ignorant-jealous denunciations one naturally detests), I take a delicate pride in.

I hold 'Irene Iddesleigh' is one of the most popular books on record. Does it not smell strange, after all the critic carving-knives used in its demolition, after 30 years it, through its peculiarity, has been placed on the shelf of Classic?

The spleen of the 'Gas-bag' section never assumed its summit until then, which proves their rotten attacks are the result of a vindictive, viperous, jealous mind I leave them to enjoy.

TO T.S. MERCER

6 February 1928

I enclose you Beer's criticism and cover of book. You will see by it that he both elevates and degrades almost every phrase. If 'Irene' is of so little use to others and of such literary unimportance, why does this aping crank trouble either about it or its humble Author?

He seems to have been conceived in a mental Hospital, then Breathed his first air somewhere about Slum St judging by his low-bred bombs which so far have been dropped, but have not taken the necessary effect until one day I'll explode them in a Critique the origin of which he will live to curse.

About my photograph, I shall have it as a silent reminder that I am the Notorious Boil on the tip of the Critics' tongues. It will appear as a frontispiece to *Helen Huddleson*.

[The reference is to Thomas Beer's introduction to the American edition of *Irene Iddesleigh*. Mercer notes that Amanda had bracketed Beer's name with the word 'Bastard'. She took further revenge in *Helen Huddleson*, where mention is made of a 'buddy called Beer, an ould scandiliser of books, no matther 'twas the Holy Bible, he'd hev somethin' dhirty til say about *it*'.]

TO T.S. MERCER

6 April 1928

I was reading recently of a very appetising price Dr Rosenbach paid for the MSS of 'Alice in Wonderland' (Mrs Hargreaves). I think this personality still lives.

Under Heaven, I ask in all sincerity, do you really think this Work worth £15,400? What think you of this money-producing Magnet of literature? Have you read 'Alice in Wonderland'? I never did. Do you know if it is still procurable?

Do you conscientiously consider it is worth such a fabulous price? It knocked me into 'Wonderland' right away and am still seriously 'wondering' if *I* should ever attain this golden goal! by a freak of fortune! If so, *you* would certainly come in for a goodly portion of the spoil.

Don't for a moment think I shall overlook all your thoughtfulness re my Works.

I think 'Six Months in Hell' wd come near this mark – should I meet with a twin Dr Rosenbach but of a more stable temperament than this example of 'Egregious Outré Monsieur'.

TO T.S. MERCER

15 April 1928

About 'Alice in Wonderland'. I have made enquiries about it but none seem to have thought it worth reading. I should indeed be glad if you cd allow me to see it. I will return it safely to you.

It is strongly suggested that Carroll is an assumed name and that the person who wrote it first was a German named 'Heiner', but I doubt if there is a single person mentioned who is genuine.

It seems Mrs Hargreaves was a little foundling found tied to a doorhandle on a poor Welshman's cottage. Whether or not there is any truth in the matter, I don't know.

However it was and is a good financial asset.

TO T.S. MERCER

4 May 1928

I thank you once again for your very nice detailed letter, also for 'Alice in Wonderland' with its lovely little gold and ruby cover.

You may rest assured I shall never part with your precious little gift, while life's lamp burns within me. I have said 'gift', but I will be very glad to pay you for it on hearing its price. I really feel so deeply in your debt already.

Don't be angry however at expressions of opinion, I consider this little Vol. apart altogether from my great appreciation of being possessor of such a largely-read work of an idiot for I hold any man wearing a clerical coat, *especially*, for a hundred and one reasons, should receive 100 strokes of the Birch to celebrate him into that region he best deserves for writing such an idiotic, nonsensical, whimsical, disjointed piece of abject happenings bursting with Stygian Style Expressions lined throughout with a pricky-patterned policy the gods would grunt at and decent-minded abhor!

I hold there isn't a child (be that child young, middle-aged or old, born since Noah was, by Godly Command, appointed Captain of that Divine Yacht shaped as an oblong meal-store into which were huddled seven other creatures, six of whom were genuine plaster-casts of Nature and from whom we virtually descend) who, in its first or second degree of childhood, could understand one solitary page of this book as it stands.

I have read hundreds of beautiful children's books by sublime Authors, but this one excels them in point of deficiency and want of efficacy. It certainly deserves the price paid for the MS inasmuch as its enormity goes to prove what most Authors practise, viz. 'gulling the majority'.

It may be I have raced over its parts too hastily to arrive at a proper estimate of its worth, but I fear further impressions are useless.

I should have liked it autographed by you. Depend however upon the fact that I appreciate none the less for forwarding it to me, and hope one day I shall be the proud writer of a Work that will yield me equally.

TO T.S. MERCER

16 August 1928

So old Barry Pain is gone — I don't feel sorry — His worldly wealth only reaching something like £1623!!!

Had I known he was such a pauper magnate I'd have treated him in a more ragged fashion than I did. Why — I'm a 'Solomon' in comparison and in my home-life as humble as a 'Working man's wife', to quote Beer.

Again – re Barry – Why, a man whose life was devoted chiefly to create laughter amongst the millions according to Press accounts, did such a 'crack celebrity' not die a Millionaire? Actually 1d. each from 1,000,000 would realise £4166.13s.4d! and this merely represents *one laugh each*!

[*See also* Amanda's poem 'The End of "Pain"' p.59]

TO T.S. MERCER

9 April 1930

The last criticism I've seen was sent me by my Bank Manager, cut from 'T.P.'s Weekly' or Post-Bag rather and headed 'An Irish Woman Realist'. I will send you this document of ups and downs which includes a slight stroke of praise! drenched to a degree by downright falsehood as I am not at all aware I ever held the abhorrent warrant for eccentricity in its meagrest mode and I consider this lying fool should be dealt with and *shall* be dealt with later along the line of time.

It seems evident he fancies I'm gone for ever from this globe of irregularities. It seems patent to me also that all the criticisms that have tried to blacken and defame me no two of which agree, aren't worthy the paper they are written on with the exception of Aldous Huxley's, *he* seems to be the only person or critic who understands my writings.

I enclose you in conjunction with this critique a cutting from a recent paper and I hold according to this critique that I should make a dart for this prize! What think you? or could you aid me in the endeavour by your valued influence as I hold according to this portion of Benjafield's *eccentric* outburst viz. 'I have many claims to have been (should that be *to be*) the *originator* of "the realistic school of fiction"' etc etc.!

I can't see that there is really any difference in Idealistic and Realistic further than the one consists chiefly of ideas formed and founded on imagination; the other consists of facts.

Could you let me know if I should try for this prize? I think it would be worth a trial.

Please let me know what *move* I should first make? or whether you could have my name entered for this huge prize?

[The article in *T.P.'s Weekly*, 9 February 1929, was signed by Louis Benjafield, after whose name, Mercer notes, Amanda had added the words 'a Pig'. He notes also that the second cutting referred to the Nobel Prize, an award of £9608 for *literature of an idealistic tendency*.]

TO T.S. MERCER

22 April 1932

I am prouder of my Works than ever; surely there must be something strangely great about my Works when they create such a furore amongst the World's noblest and best down to the 'Hogwashing Hooligans' whose sole foundation is based upon spleen.

I pity such poor apes.

TO NORMAN CARROTHERS

14 April 1932

I write to thank you for your great thoughtfulness and kindness in calling to present me with 'The Children of the Abbey', a book dearer to me than any existing work, more so by its dress of black and gold. . . I have numerous gifts of books given personally to me. Quite recently a gentleman friend in London sent me a specially got-up volume, 'Alice in Wonderland', garbed in maroon and gold. I read it every line and my opinion about it is its beautiful garb is absolutely lost cloaking its idiotic pages, and that 'hogwashing' critic who found time to whiff its pages' with the wind of irony should be stoned to death for trying to deceive the public with such lines of drunken bluff. When I finished its perusal I could not recall one redeeming feature of elegance from cover to cover. It is so descriptive of some old clergyman in his smallest of years trying to make up a sermon of very irregular infantisms. Enough of 'Alice in Wonderland', save that the gulled American who paid £15,000 for such rubbish must have been a warder over a gang of weaklings for an indefinite period, when he too became infected with their idiotisms.

But on the other hand if this purchaser had handed me this sum, I would have criticised him a first-class exhibitor of brainfulness.

I see a criticism in 'The Irish News' of the 8th inst. by some *donkeyosity* who calls himself Billy Moore and whom I style 'Hogwash'. He must be a greenhorn and addicted to browsing on heather. I feel very proud to think 'Irene Iddesleigh' is not yet dead but is very much alive, this proving that worth so few of her contemporaries enjoy. This book has caused more publicity than any other work I know and is as live to criticism as the day it first smote the *Aristocratic* Public and Nobility throughout the five continents, of which I have practical proof, and mark you, 'Hogwash' rolls himself up in a cloak of conquer feeding himself with a wee bit assurance that this 'Blurby Plaster' will be the death of 'Irene Iddesleigh'. . . .

TO NORMAN CARROTHERS

28 October 1932

I am sitting here meditating very seriously whether or not I ever thanked you for your two books sent to me on 1 May last. I am extremely interested in both volumes, especially Oscar Wilde. I have just finished reading 'The Ballad of Reading Jail', with indescribable admiration and sympathetic tremor. I take it to be the best work of its kind ever written. I am in strong sympathy with Oscar and believe were the World better stocked with clever characters such as he, fewer cuddies there would be browsing on the dole. I thank you from the pores of a heart stuffed with admiration for these two works, particularly Oscar Wilde, the tame tragedian.

I was a little perturbed at the idea of entertaining your friends in this small old cottage two hundred years old, just about the age of all your friends clashed together on that memorable day coupled with joy and sorrow; sorrow because I could not sufficiently entertain your friends as I should have liked in my confined quarters, but I hope that at no distant date we shall all meet at Larne in my home, where you will be much better attended to and have more breathing space to talk volubly; joy because of the gentlemen who formed a cabal I appreciated in full, especially Mr Desmond MacCarthy, if I spell his Christian name properly, if not, I sit corrected.

On meeting this aristocratic son of – let me presume – Irish Soil, I was more interested in his manner and bearing than the others. When introduced to him, his fine refulgent eyes seemed cloaked around with the most expressive symbol of gladness – I presume at meeting me – I have ever witnessed in any personality. . . He appears to have an overstocked brain which at times he leisurely develops for the admiration of others – on a whole he seems one great luminary in the art of tragedy, in fact – a Shakespeare, only void of Shakespearean coldness and affected sublimity. . .

I enclose a snapshot of that wonderful personality who has disturbed the bowels of the millions! I was snapped by Eileen Johnston at Bangor Hospital along with my younger sister, Emma, who was Matron of Bangor Hospital then. This photo has undergone many journeys by post – England, Spain, Connecticut, Edinburgh, Eton, Oxford, Balliol and many such throughout the realms of space. I shall have my photo taken at no distant date in order to satisfy the many admirers thirsting for a glimpse of her the Hell-deserving rodents of damning assumption and ignorance have tried their utmost to char and silence: but little do these slashers of talent (weak or strong), these drunken make-believes dream that which awaits them by her pen.

I must to a certain degree hold with a corner of my 'Dam of Disdain' a veritable pond of affection for that class of cleanly-minded men called 'Critics of Honour', that class who really careth not to use the carving knife of knavery or sycophantic spleen to satisfy a dirty-minded few who would glory in cutting the wings of Christ were he to grace Earth again with his Lordly Presence. Take, for instance, Aldous Huxley, Sir E.V. Lucas, Charles Howden, John Lyle Donaghy and Kenmuir and compare their separate criticisms with those of St Scandalbags (Lewis) or Barry Pain, who presumably now enjoys himself criticising his beloved Satan in his Mansions of Flare.

TO NORMAN CARROTHERS

21 November 1932

I am busy writing the final chapters of 'Helen Huddleson' for Mr Mercer, who types all my works. I will be very busy until I finish the book which one day I hope will appear in theatrical form upon the platform of talent – afterwards to be hung upon the Gallows of Fate to the consternation of all admirers in general and delight of its murders (the bloody blinkers of talent) in particular.

I think Friday is your day of collecting souls and discussing matters, so I think I am well entitled to let you have a glance at a page or two of 'Helen' to satisfy your amiable clique of highly-bred. How very much I admire the French and Americans as a slap in the face for Tom Beer, the American ringleader amongst the loose, who has used the tarbrush of traitorism against 'Irene Iddesleigh'.

I remember someone mentioned to me about a gentleman named Meredith who, I gathered, was a Professor in Queen's College, so if you wish you can let him have a glance at this chapter, as I am persuaded to believe he admires something wild and stirring in books.

TO NORMAN CARROTHERS

8 December 1933

I see my name mentioned in this week's 'Newsletter', as it seems the late Lord Oxford mentioned me in his writings. I expect I will be talked about at the end of 1000 years.

TO NORMAN CARROTHERS

5 March 1934

The very heart and soul is harassed out of me by my lawyer, trying to better himself largely at my expense. I feel getting weaker and more worried every day and, dear Mr Carrothers, I wish to God you would come down on Sat. evg. until I confide in you. . . I am wondering if you could bring a lawyer whom you know intimately, I mean one on whom you could rely, along with you until I would unveil how I am being imposed upon. He could accompany you but perhaps it would be better not to say I wrote you to bring him. You could just ask him to come with you for company, one which you consider clever and well up in law, and not an old one with old ideas, as there are always new laws and new rules coming out every day. . . I will have a good tea for you both.

NORMAN CARROTHERS

9 September 1934

I would be glad to see the critique you mention which appeared in the 'Daily Express', no matter how bad the beast described his effortless effort to sting the Author, who loves to see she can wring from the critic-crabs their biting little bits of buggery! Every critique you see, cut it out and let me have it, if you please.

14 May 1936

I am back in the old house once more and shall be until the Master calls me home and places me in a kindly nook of his vast mansions, but indeed if I get slipped into a small snug bungalow where there will be plenty of ink – a pen – and writing pads, I will be content.

[The 'old house' was Iddesleigh, Larne, County Antrim. The other letters to Norman Carrothers printed here came from Ballynahinch, County Down, where Amanda had lived with her second husband, Thomas Rodgers, since 1922. She returned to Larne at the end of 1935, a few years after his death.]

· AT HOME · ALWAYS TO THE HONOURABLE.

Mrs Amanda M Ros,

AUTHORESS

Iddesleigh,
Ireland.

Telegrams
·· Iddesleigh, Ireland.''

FAREWELL

Farewell to all my friends and foes,
When again we'll meet—God knows!
However, should it be Above,
Where nought abides but Holy Love,
I'll greet you with a saintly smile
That e'en the Devil would beguile:
Perchance it should be down below,
I'll grin at every one I know,
And if our lot be in between,
I'll bless the Pope and curse the King.

SELECT BIBLIOGRAPHY

BY AMANDA McKITTRICK ROS

Irene Iddesleigh, Belfast, privately published, 1897; London, Nonesuch
Press, 1926; New York, Boni & Liveright, 1927
Delina Delaney, Belfast, privately published, 1898; London, Chatto &
Windus, 1935
Poems of Puncture, London, Arthur H. Stockwell, *c.* 1912
Kaiser Bill! (broadsheet), *c.* 1915
A Little Belgian Orphan (broadsheet, signed pseudonymously Monica
Moyland, Larne, Irelande), 1916
Fumes of Formation, Belfast, R. Carswell & Son, 1933
Bayonets of Bastard Sheen, Thames Ditton, privately published, 1949
*St Scandalbags together with Meet Irene by D.B. Wyndham Lewis &
At the Sign of the Harrow by F. Anstey,* edited and with notes by
T. Stanley Mercer, Thames Ditton, Merle Press, 1954
Donald Dudley, The Bastard Critic, Thames Ditton, Merle Press, 1954
Helen Huddleson, edited and with an introduction by Jack Loudan, who
provides a concluding chapter, London, Chatto & Windus, 1969

ABOUT AMANDA McKITTRICK ROS

Huxley, Aldous. 'Euphues Redivivus', *On the Margin,* London, Chatto &
Windus, 1923
Loudan, Jack. *O Rare Amanda!,* London, Chatto & Windus, 1954

NOTE

On the title page of *Poems of Puncture* Mrs Ros claims authorship of
three works entitled 'The Hedge Round Hell', 'The Lusty Lawyer' and
'Motherless Moon'. None of these was ever published and the first two
titles are among the many fragments of her projected novel 'Six Months
in Hell'.

ACKNOWLEDGEMENTS

Grateful acknowledgement is made to the estate of Amanda McKittrick Ros and Chatto & Windus; to R.G. Crothers on behalf of the estate of Amanda McKittrick Ros; to Rory Johnston on behalf of the estate of Denis Johnston; and to the Peters Fraser & Dunlop Group Ltd for permission to reprint 'Meet Irene' by D.B. Wyndham Lewis.